Applied Probability
Control
Economics
Information and Communication
Modeling and Identification
Numerical Techniques
Optimization

Applications of Mathematics

15

Edited by   A. V. Balakrishnan

Advisory Board   E. Dynkin
G. Kallianpur
R. Radner

N. U. Prabhu

Stochastic Storage Processes

Queues, Insurance Risk, and Dams

Springer-Verlag
New York Heidelberg Berlin

N. U. Prabhu
School of Operations Research
Cornell University
Ithaca, NY 14853
USA

Editor

A. V. Balakrishnan
University of California
Systems Science Department
Los Angeles, CA 90024
USA

AMS Subject Classifications (1980): Primary 60K30; Secondary 60G20, 60K25, 62P05, 62P99

Library of Congress Cataloging in Publication Data

Prabhu, Narahari Umanath, 1924-
  Stochastic storage processes.

  (Applications of mathematics; 15)
  Bibliography: p.
  Includes index.
  1. Queuing theory. 2. Stochastic processes.
I. Title.
T57.9.P63   519.8'2   80-18686

All rights reserved.

No part of this book may be translated or reproduced in any form without written permission from Springer-Verlag.

© 1980 by Springer-Verlag New York Inc.

Printed in the United States of America.

9 8 7 6 5 4 3 2 1

ISBN 0-387-90522-7 Springer-Verlag New York
ISBN 3-540-90522-7 Springer-Verlag Berlin Heidelberg

To All of My Students

Preface

This book is based on a course I have taught at Cornell University since 1965. The primary topic of this course was queueing theory, but related topics such as inventories, insurance risk, and dams were also included. As a text I used my earlier book, *Queues and Inventories* (John Wiley, New York, 1965). Over the years the emphasis in this course shifted from detailed analysis of probability models to the study of stochastic processes that arise from them, and the subtitle of the text, "A Study of Their Basic Stochastic Processes," became a more appropriate description of the course. My own research into the fluctuation theory for Lévy processes provided a new perspective on the topics discussed, and enabled me to reorganize the material. The lecture notes used for the course went through several versions, and the final version became this book. A detailed description of my approach will be found in the Introduction.

I have not attempted to give credit to authors of individual results. Readers interested in the historical literature should consult the Selected Bibliography given at the end of the Introduction. The original work in this area is presented here with simpler proofs that make full use of the special features of the underlying stochastic processes. The same approach makes it possible to provide several new results.

Thanks are due to Kathy King for her excellent typing of the manuscript. To my wife Sumi goes my sincere appreciation for her constant encouragement, especially during the preparation of the last chapter. Finally, I have dedicated this book to all of my students: their questions, comments, and criticism have made a significant contribution to the presentation.

Ithaca, New York N. U. Prabhu
November 1980

Contents

Abbreviations and Notation	xi
Introduction	1
1 A Class of Stochastic Models	1
2 Problems Arising from the Models	6
3 The Scope of this Book	7
4 Further Remarks	8
Problems	10
Selected Bibliography	13

Part I
The Single Server Queue — 17

Chapter 1
The Queue G/G/1 and the Associated Random Walk — 19

1 Orientation	19
2 Ladder Processes	21
3 Two Renewal Functions	23
4 Maximum and Minimum	24
5 Application to the Queue G/G/1	27
6 The Queue M/M/1	32
7 The Queues G/M/1 and M/G/1	34
8 Application to Queue Length	38
9 Further Remarks	43
Problems	44

Chapter 2
Further Results for the Queue G/G/1 — 48

1 Transforms	48
2 Further Applications to the Queue G/G/1	53
3 The Queues G/M/1 and M/G/1	56
4 The Queue $G/E_k/1$	58
5 The Queue $E_k/G/1$	61
Problems	62
References	63

Part II
Continuous Time Storage Models 65

Chapter 3
The Basic Storage Model 67

1 Orientation 67
2 Lévy Processes 69
3 A Generalized Storage Model 73
4 A First Passage Time 79
5 Insurance Risk: Two Special Cases 85
6 The Ladder Epochs $\{T_k^*\}$ 86
7 Limit Theorems for the Storage Model 89
8 A Second Storage Model 92
9 The Queue G/M/1 95
10 Queues with Static Priorities 99
11 Queues with Dynamic Priorities 102
   Problems 105

Chapter 4
More Storage Models 108

1 Introduction 108
2 Ladder Points for a Two-Dimensional Random Walk 111
3 Ladder Points for Processes of Class $\mathscr{L}_+$ 112
4 Properties of Processes of Class $\mathscr{L}_+ \cup \mathscr{L}_-$ 113
5 The Insurance Risk Problem: General Case 119
6 The Queue M/M/1 120
7 A Storage Model with Random Output 124
8 Further Remarks 128
   Problems 131
   References 133

Appendix 135

Index 137

Abbreviations and Notation

Abbreviations

Term	Abbreviation
Characteristic function	c.f.
Distribution function	d.f.
If and only if	Iff
Laplace transform	L.T.
Probability generating function	p.g.f.

The term *transform* is used for expressions such as $E(z^N e^{-\theta X})$ where N is integer-valued and $X \geq 0$. The notation F is used both for a distribution measure and a d.f., leading to the use of $F(dx)$ and $dF(x)$ respectively.

Notations

1. *The normal d.f.*

$$N(x) = \int_{-\infty}^{x} \frac{1}{\sqrt{2\pi}} e^{-1/2 y^2} \, dy \quad (-\infty < x < \infty).$$

2. *One sided normal d.f.'s*

   (i) $\quad N_+(x) = 0 \qquad$ for $x \leq 0,$
   $\quad\quad\;\; N_+(x) = 2N(x) - 1 \quad$ for $x \geq 0.$

   This distribution has mean $= \sqrt{2/\pi}$ and variance $= 1 - 2/\pi$.

(ii)
$$N_-(x) = 2N(x) \quad \text{for } x \leq 0$$
$$N_-(x) = 1 \quad \text{for } x \geq 0.$$

If the random variable x has d.f. N_+, then $-x$ has d.f. N_-.

3. *Stable d.f. with exponent $\frac{1}{2}$*

$$G_{1/2}(x) = 0 \quad \text{for } x \leq 0,$$
$$G_{1/2}(x) = 2\left[1 - N\left(\frac{1}{\sqrt{x}}\right)\right] \quad \text{for } x \geq 0.$$

This distribution is more easily recognized by its density, which is given by

$$g_{1/2}(x) = 0 \quad \text{for } x \leq 0,$$
$$g_{1/2}(x) = \frac{1}{\sqrt{2\pi x^3}} e^{-1/2x} \quad \text{for } x \geq 0$$

or by its Laplace transform, which is $e^{-\sqrt{2\theta}}$ ($\theta > 0$). The mean of the distribution is ∞.

Introduction

1 A Class of Stochastic Models

The processes investigated in this book are those arising from stochastic models for queues, inventories, dams, insurance risk, and other situations. The following brief description of some of these models will make it clear that the common title "storage processes" is appropriate for these processes.

1.1 The Single-Server Queueing System

A server (or counter) provides a certain service. Customers seeking this service arrive successively at the epochs $t_0(=0)$, t_1, t_2, ..., so that $u_k = t_k - t_{k-1}$ ($k \geq 1$) are their inter-arrival times. The amounts of time spent by these customers at the counter receiving service are called their service times. Let $v_1, v_2, \ldots$ be the service times of the successive customers. We assume that $\{u_k, k \geq 1\}$ and $\{v_k, k \geq 1\}$ are two independent renewal sequences; that is, (i) $u_1, u_2, \ldots$ are mutually independent random variables with a common d.f. $A(u)$, (ii) $v_1, v_2, \ldots$ are mutually independent random variables with a common d.f. $B(v)$, and (iii) u_k and v_k are mutually independent. The customers' behavior in the system is governed by the specification of a queue discipline. In particular, under the "first come, first served" discipline, customers line up in the order of arrival and receive service in that order.

Let W_n be the nth customer's waiting time: that is, the time he will have to wait for commencement of his service. We wish to investigate the stochastic process $\{W_n, n \geq 0\}$. In order to do this let us consider the customers

1

C_n and C_{n+1} who arrive at the epochs t_n and t_{n+1} respectively. Customer C_n will reach the counter at time $t_n + W_n$ and will complete his service and leave the system at time $D_{n+1} = t_n + W_n + v_{n+1}$. If $t_{n+1} < D_{n+1}$, then it is clear that C_{n+1}'s waiting time is given by $W_{n+1} = D_{n+1} - t_{n+1}$, while if $t_{n+1} \geq D_{n+1}$, then $W_{n+1} = 0$. We have

$$D_{n+1} - t_{n+1} = W_n + v_{n+1} - (t_{n+1} - t_n)$$
$$= W_n + v_{n+1} - u_{n+1}.$$

Denoting $X_n = v_n - u_n$ $(n \geq 1)$ we therefore find that

$$W_{n+1} = W_n + X_{n+1} \quad \text{if } W_n + X_{n+1} > 0$$
$$= 0 \quad \text{if } W_n + X_{n+1} \leq 0.$$

We can write these equations as

$$W_{n+1} = \max(0, W_n + X_{n+1}). \tag{1}$$

We shall also consider the random variables I_n $(n \geq 1)$, where I_n is the idle time (if any) preceding the nth arrival. The arguments that led to (1) also show that

$$I_{n+1} = -\min(0, W_n + X_{n+1}). \tag{2}$$

Equations (1)–(2) provide the starting point for our study of the queueing system. It turns out that the properties of the processes $\{W_n\}$ and $\{I_n\}$ can be obtained from those of the random walk $\{S_n, n \geq 0\}$, where

$$S_0 \equiv 0, \quad S_n = X_1 + X_2 + \cdots + X_n \quad (n \geq 1).$$

EXAMPLE (The Simple Queue). Here

$$A(x) = 1 - e^{-\lambda x}, \quad B(x) = 1 - e^{-\mu x}, \tag{3}$$

where $0 < \lambda < \infty$, $0 < \mu < \infty$. In spite of the simplicity of these distributions, this case cannot be treated in an elementary manner as far as equations (1) and (2) are concerned, and we have to depend on the general theory. However, instead of waiting times of customers, let us consider $Q(t)$, the number of customers present in the system at time t, including the one being served (if any). Let $N_1(t)$ be the number of customers who arrive at the system during the time interval $(0, t]$; from (3) we see that $N_1(t)$ is a simple Poisson process with parameter λ. Also, let us denote by $N_2(t)$ a simple Poisson process with parameter μ, which is independent of $N_1(t)$. Then we can represent $Q(t)$ as follows:

$$Q(t) = Q(0) + N_1(t) - \int_0^t 1_{Q(s-)>0} \, dN_2(s), \tag{4}$$

where 1_E is the indicator function of the event E. We can investigate the properties of $Q(t)$ using (4), and obtain the distribution of waiting times from $Q(t)$.

1.2 Inventory Models

An inventory is an amount of material stored for the purpose of future sale or production. In discrete time the inventory function Z_n is defined by the recurrence relation

$$Z_{n+1} = Z_n + \eta_{n+1} - f(Z_n + \eta_{n+1}, \xi_{n+1}), \tag{5}$$

where η_{n+1} is the amount ordered at time $n + 1$, ξ_{n+1} the demand for the material during $(n, n + 1]$, and $f(Z_n + \eta_{n+1}, \xi_{n+1})$ is the amount sold at time $n + 1$. In the standard case it is assumed that the successive demands $\xi_1, \xi_2, \ldots$ are mutually independent random variables with a common distribution, and orders are placed in accordance with a specified ordering policy and the function f is prescribed by this policy. Clearly, $f(Z_n + \eta_{n+1}, \xi_{n+1}) \leq \xi_{n+1}$. Two types of ordering policies may be considered, allowing for $f(Z_n + \eta_{n+1}, \xi_{n+1}) > Z_n + \eta_{n+1}$ or not.

(a) *Backlog Allowed.* Here $f(Z_n + \eta_{n+1}, \xi_{n+1}) = \xi_{n+1}$. The equation (5) becomes

$$Z_{n+1} = Z_n + \eta_{n+1} - \xi_{n+1}, \tag{6}$$

a negative inventory level indicating a backlog. The amount of backlog at time $n + 1$ is given by

$$\begin{aligned} B_{n+1} &= \max(0, -Z_{n+1}) \\ &= -\min(0, Z_n + \eta_{n+1} - \xi_{n+1}). \end{aligned} \tag{7}$$

(b) *No Backlog Allowed.* Here demands are met "if physically possible," so that

$$f(Z_n + \eta_{n+1}, \xi_{n+1}) = \min(Z_n + \eta_{n+1}, \xi_{n+1}). \tag{8}$$

We can then write (5) as

$$Z_{n+1} = \max(0, Z_n + \eta_{n+1} - \xi_{n+1}). \tag{9}$$

This policy results in deficits, the amount of deficit at time $n + 1$ being given by

$$\begin{aligned} D_{n+1} &= \xi_{n+1} - f(Z_n + \eta_{n+1}, \xi_{n+1}) \\ &= -\min(0, Z_n + \eta_{n+1} - \xi_{n+1}). \end{aligned} \tag{10}$$

EXAMPLE i (An Inventory Model of the (s, S) Type). This is described as follows. Two real numbers s, S are given, where $0 \leq s < S < \infty$. The amount sold always equals the demand. Whenever the inventory level falls below s, an order is placed to bring up the level to S, but otherwise no ordering is done. Thus the amount ordered is given by

$$\begin{aligned} \eta_{n+1} &= 0 \quad &&\text{if } s \leq Z_n \leq S \\ &= S - Z_n \quad &&\text{if } Z_n < s. \end{aligned} \tag{11}$$

The equation (5) reduces, in this model, to

$$Z_{n+1} = Z_n - \xi_{n+1} \quad \text{if } s \leq Z_n \leq S$$
$$= S - \xi_{n+1} \quad \text{if } Z_n < s. \tag{12}$$

In the inventory model described above it is assumed that the supply of material is under control in the sense that the exact amount ordered will be always supplied, except perhaps with a delay or time lag. However, there are situations in which this supply is also a random variable.

EXAMPLE ii (A Monotone Ordering Policy). This is described by a critical number x^*, and the ordering policy is as follows: If the inventory level $Z_n \geq x^*$, no ordering is done. If $Z_n < x^*$, then an order is placed, and a random amount (say X_{n+1}) of material is delivered immediately. Thus

$$Z_{n+1} = Z_n + X_{n+1} - \xi_{n+1} \quad \text{if } Z_n < x^*$$
$$= Z_n - \xi_{n+1} \quad \text{if } Z_n \geq x^*, \tag{13}$$

where the demand ξ_{n+1} is also a random variable.

1.3 Storage Models

The inventory models described above are characterized by an ordering policy, the supply of material being under control or subject to randomness. We now describe a class of models in which both the supply of material (the input) and the demand (output) are random variables, and the objective is to regulate the demand so as to achieve a storage of desirable level. We may call these input-output models or storage models.

EXAMPLE i (Models for a Finite Dam). Let X_{n+1} be the amount of water that has flowed into the dam (the input) during the period $(n, n+1]$ ($n \geq 0$). We assume that $X_1, X_2, \ldots$ are mutually independent random variables with a common distribution. Because of the finite capacity (say c) of the dam there is an overflow, and the actual input after the overflow equals

$$\eta_{n+1} = \min(X_{n+1}, c - Z_n), \tag{14}$$

where Z_n is the storage level at time n. Demands for water occur at times $n = 1, 2, \ldots$, the amount of demand (the output) at time n being ξ_n. We assume that $\xi_1, \xi_2, \ldots$ are mutually independent random variables with a common distribution, and that the ξ_n are independent of the X_n. The storage policy prescribes the following release rule for water:

$$f(Z_n + \eta_{n+1}, \xi_{n+1}) = \min(Z_n + \eta_{n+1}, \xi_{n+1}). \tag{15}$$

1 A Class of Stochastic Models

The equation (5) then becomes

$$Z_{n+1} = \max(0, Z_n + \eta_{n+1} - \xi_{n+1}). \tag{16}$$

EXAMPLE ii (The Single-Server Queue). The comparison of (16) with the recurrence relations (1) for the waiting times W_n shows that the single-server queueing model is analogous to the storage model in which the u_n represent input and v_n the output. The storage policy does not allow backlogs.

1.4 Insurance Risk

The theory of insurance risk is concerned with the business of an insurance company, subject to the following assumptions: (i) the total amount $X(t)$ of claims that occur during a time interval $(0, t]$ has the compound Poisson distribution

$$K(x, t) = \sum_{n=0}^{\infty} e^{-\lambda t} \frac{(\lambda t)^n}{n!} P_n(x) \quad (-\infty < x < \infty), \tag{17}$$

negative claims arising in the case of ordinary whole-life annuities. (ii) The company receives premiums at a constant rate β $(-\infty < \beta < \infty)$. The function

$$Z(t) = x + \beta t - X(t) \tag{18}$$

is called the risk reserve, with the initial value $Z(0) = x \geq 0$. When this reserve becomes negative, the company is ruined. This event happens at the epoch $T \equiv T(x)$, where

$$T = \inf\{t : Z(t) < 0\}. \tag{19}$$

The main concern of the theory is the distribution of the random variable T (the so-called ruin problem). The company is interested in choosing the initial reserve large enough to avoid ruin over a finite or infinite time span, with a specified probability. Thus it is required to find x such that either

$$P\{T(x) > t\} \geq \alpha \quad \text{or} \quad P\{T(x) = \infty\} \geq \alpha \quad (0 < \alpha < 1). \tag{20}$$

1.5 Continuous Time Inventory and Storage Models

The inventory and storage models described above are all formulated in discrete time. The risk reserve (18) provides an example (in the case where $\beta > 0$ and $X(t) > 0$) of an inventory function in which during a time interval $(0, t]$ the amount supplied is βt and the demand is $X(t)$. As an example of a continuous time storage process, let us consider the following model for the dam. Let $X(t)$ denote the amount of water which has flowed into the dam (the input) during a time interval $(0, t]$; we assume that $X(t)$ is a Lévy process. The release is at a rate $r \equiv r[Z(t)]$ where $Z(t)$ is the amount of water in the dam at time t. Here $r(x)$ is a continuous nondecreasing function for $x > 0$, and $r(0) = 0$. We have then

$$Z(t) = Z(0) + X(t) - \int_0^t r[Z(s)]\, ds, \qquad (21)$$

which is an integral equation for $Z(t)$. The integral in (21) represents the total amount of water released during $(0, t]$. As a special case if we take

$$r(x) = 1 \quad \text{for } x > 0, \qquad (22)$$
$$ = 0 \quad \text{for } x = 0,$$

then this model is analogous to the discrete time model of Moran described above, with capacity $c = \infty$.

Comparison of (21) with the equation (4) for the queue length $Q(t)$ shows that $Q(t)$ can be viewed as a storage process with the Poisson input $N_1(t)$, and the release occurring at random epochs given by the successive events of the Poisson process $N_2(t)$.

2 Problems Arising from the Models

The main objectives of the analysis of models described above are the following.

(a) *The Study of the Basic Stochastic Processes.* It is clear that the probability assumptions underlying the models give rise to a stochastic process in each case. Thus we have the waiting time process $\{W_n\}$ in the single-server queueing system, the inventory level $\{Z_n\}$, and the risk reserve $\{Z(t), t \geq 0\}$. We shall designate every such process as a storage process. An investigation of this process is essential for a proper understanding of the system described by the model.

(b) *Statistical Inference.* The underlying probability distributions are very often unspecified or else specified but for a certain number of parameters. It is then required to estimate the unknown distributions or parameters from observation of the storage process over a time interval of fixed or random length. Similarly, tests of hypotheses concerning these distributions or parameters may also have to be carried out on the basis of such an observation.

(c) *Design and Control Problems.* The operation of a system of the type described in section 1 yields revenues, but of course costs are also incurred. It is then desired to find the most economical policy of running the system. For example, in an inventory system the revenue is from the material sold, while the costs are storage and ordering costs, penalty for unfilled demands and so on; the problem is then to find an ordering policy that maximizes the profit (revenue minus costs). Optimization problems such as this are concerned with the design of the system, and may be characterized as deterministic control problems in the sense that once the optimal design is found, the system so designed is allowed to run subject only to the basic assumptions. On the other hand, stochastic control problems arise when the objective is to run the system with a set of rules specifying actions to be taken from time to time, on the basis of past observations. For example, in a queueing system these actions might be admission or rejection of an arriving customer, increasing or decreasing the service rate, etc.

It must be understood that the three classes of problems described above are closely connected. Thus we may minimize the "long run" cost of operating the system (that is, the cost when the process has reached a steady state). Also the estimates mentioned in (b) are obtained from statistical data collected from a system that is already in operation, the purpose of estimation being the design of better (more efficient) systems in the future.

3 The Scope of this Book

The main classes of models investigated in this book are queueing, insurance risk, and dams. We study the stochastic processes underlying these models; inference and control problems will be investigated in a later volume. These processes are usually (but not always) Markovian—in particular, random walks and Lévy processes. In order to answer important questions concerning our models we investigate various aspects of our processes such as the maximum and minimum functionals and hitting times. Our approach is based on the recurrence relation (1) and the integral equation (21), rather than the use of standard properties of these processes. Specifically, we use the fluctuation theory of random walks and Lévy processes, in which Wiener–Hopf factorization plays a central role.

The book is in two parts. In part I we present the theory of single-server queues with the first come, first served discipline, using the fluctuation theory of the underlying random walk. The results described here provide answers to most of the important questions concerning this general system, but in special cases of Poisson arrivals or exponential service time density, or systems with priority queue disciplines, there still remain some questions. These latter are more appropriately formulated within the framework of continuous time storage models, a theory of which is developed in part II. The class of models investigated here also includes those for insurance risk and dams, the underlying processes being a class of Lévy processes. One group of models are formulated in terms of the integral equation (21) with $r(x)$ as in (22), and analyzed by special techniques that are available for this case. For more general storage models the analysis uses the properties of ladder processes associated with the basic Lévy process. The treatment emphasizes the common features of the relevant problems. Apart from achieving economy of presentation it is hoped that this unified approach would also encourage a perspective on this vast area of stochastic models.

4 Further Remarks

4.1 Queues

The modern probability theory of queues owes a great deal to the two fundamental papers by Kendall (1951, 1953). References to earlier pioneer work will be found in these two papers. Kendall introduced the notation GI/G/1 for the single-server system described in section 1. In this book we shall use the slightly changed notation G/G/1. Here the first G indicates that the inter-arrival times have an arbitrary distribution, the second G that the service times have an arbitrary distribution, and 1 indicates that the system has one server. The so-called simple queue of the example of section 1 is then denoted as M/M/1, where M denotes the Markov (lack of memory) property of the arrival process and the service times. Other special systems are (i) M/G/1 where the inter-arrival times have an exponential density (so that the arrival process is Poisson), and (ii) G/M/1 where the service times have an exponential density.

So far we have assumed the queue discipline to be "first come, first served." We now define a discipline based on priorities. Suppose that customers arriving in a single-server system are divided into two mutually exclusive and exhaustive classes numbered 0 and 1, in such a way that a customer of class 1 is always served prior to a customer of class 0. Within each class the queue discipline is "first come, first served." A class 1 customer arriving when no other customers of his class are present may either go directly into service displacing the customer (if any) of class 0 being served, or wait till this customer completes his service. In the first case we have pre-emptive discipline and in the second case head-of-the-line discipline. In the pre-emptive case the displaced customer (of class 0) returns to the head of the queue of his class and waits until the newly arrived customer and other subsequent arrivals of class 1 are served. When this happens he may either resume his service from where it was interrupted, or repeat his service from the start. The queue discipline thus described is based on static priorities, namely, the priorities are determined before the customers' arrival. We shall also consider dynamic priorities.

4 Further Remarks

4.2 Inventory Models

Inventory problems are very important in economics and in business administration and have received considerable attention. For a systematic study of the classical models see Arrow, Karlin, and Scarf (1958). A unified modern treatment will be found in the book by Tijms (1972). In more recent work the basic model described in section 1 has been extended in many respects. The dominant theme in this area is the optimization problem.

4.3 Models for Dams

Empirical work on the determination of storage capacity was done by Hurst (1951, 1956). Earlier, Massé (1946) gave a formulation of the optimum storage problem along the following lines: Demand is either for electric power (expressed in terms of the volume of water required to produce it) or for water to be supplied to a city. It is assumed that supplementary sources exist (a thermal station or an arrangement for borrowing water from a nearby dam) in case the entire demand cannot be fully met, but these are available at a cost, and moreover, may be available only up to a certain limit. Little (1955) studied the problem with reference to the Grand Coulee Dam—see also Koopmans (1958). In 1954 P. A. P. Moran formulated his probability theory of a dam, which was later developed further and extended by him and several other authors. In this theory the demand $\xi_{n+1} \equiv m$ ($< c$); more realistic release rules have been suggested by H. W. Holdaway [see Moran (1959)]. An account of the theory covering developments up to 1965 has been given by Prabhu (1965).

4.4 Insurance Risk

Risk theory had its beginnings in the probability models for the operation of a non-life insurance business proposed by T. Barrois (1835), E. Dormoy (1878), and others. The classical theory, originally called collective risk theory, emerged with F. Lundberg's 1903 doctoral thesis at Uppsala University, and developed rapidly through a series of papers published by him and other Swedish actuaries. A survey of the theory from the point of view of stochastic processes was given by Cramér (1954, 1955). A comprehensive account, emphasizing the mathematical and statistical aspects, was given by Seal (1969). In a recent monograph Seal (1978) also presents numerical results for the company's survival over a finite time span. These two books by Seal contains the references to the papers mentioned earlier. The title "insurance risk" would seem to be more appropriate for this theory and will be used in this book.

Problems

1. In the inventory model of (s, S) type, let $G_n(x)$ be the d.f. of $\xi_1 + \xi_2 + \cdots + \xi_n$ $(n \geq 1)$, and

$$H_n(x) = \int_{0-}^{\Delta} dG_{n-1}(y)[1 - G_1(S - x - y)] \qquad (n \geq 1),$$

where $\Delta = S - s > 0$ and $G_0(x) = 0$ for $x < 0$, and $= 1$ for $x \geq 0$. Assume that $Z_0 < s$, and let $F_n(x) = P\{Z_n < x\}$ $(n \geq 1)$. Prove the following:

(i) $F_n(x) = \sum_{m=1}^{n} u_{n-m} H_m(x)$, where $u_n = F_n(s)$.

(ii) $\lim_{n \to \infty} F_n(x) = \dfrac{\sum_{1}^{\infty} H_m(x)}{\sum_{0}^{\infty} G_n(\Delta)}$.

2. Continuation. Let the demand ξ_n have the density $\mu e^{-\mu x}$ $(0 < \mu < \infty)$.

(i) Show that

$$\lim_{n \to \infty} F_n(x) = \frac{e^{-\mu(s-x)}}{1 + \mu\Delta} \qquad \text{for } x < s$$

$$= \frac{1 + \mu(x-s)}{1 + \mu\Delta} \qquad \text{for } s \leq x \leq S.$$

(ii) The associated costs are as follows:
Ordering cost for an amount x of material $= c_1 x + c_2 G_0(x)$,
penalty cost per unit deficit $= p$,
storage cost per unit $= h$.
Show that the long run cost function is a minimum when

$$\Delta = \sqrt{\frac{2c_2}{h\mu}}$$

$$e^{-\mu s_0} = \frac{h + \sqrt{2c_2 h\mu}}{h + p} \qquad \text{if } \sqrt{2c_2 h\mu} < p$$

$$= 1 \qquad \text{if } \sqrt{2c_2 h\mu} \geq p.$$

3. A Grain Storage Model. Let X_{n+1} be the yield of grain during the year $(n, n+1]$, and assume that $X_1, X_2, \ldots$ are mutually independent random variables with a common distribution. Suppose that it is decided to store a proportion α $(0 < \alpha < 1)$ of the amount of grain available during any year for future use. Let Z_n be the amount stored during $(n, n+1]$, with $Z_0 \equiv 0$.

(i) Prove that $\lim_{n \to \infty} Z_n = Z$ exists with probability one, where the random variable Z has the same distribution as $\sum_{1}^{\infty} \alpha^r X_r$.

(ii) The cost function is given by

$$L(Z_n) = c_1 Z_n + c_2 (Y_{n+1} - m)^2,$$

where c_1 = cost of storage per unit, c_2 is a constant, $Y_{n+1} = (1 - \alpha) \times (Z_n + X_{n+1})$ is the amount released for sale during $(n, n+1]$, and m is a "desirable level" of release. Show that the value of α that minimizes the expected cost in the long run is given by

$$\hat{\alpha} = \frac{1 - \sqrt{d}}{1 + \sqrt{d}} \quad \text{if } d < 1,$$

$$= 0 \quad \text{if } d \geq 1,$$

where $d = c_1 \mu / 2 c_2 \sigma^2$, $\mu = E(X_n)$ and $\sigma^2 = \text{Var}(X_n)$.

4. **Replacements at Random Times.** Consider a warehouse with capacity c $(0 < c < \infty)$, where deliveries of material are made at arbitrary epochs of time, the time intervals between successive deliveries being mutually independent random variables with a common d.f. $A(x)$. Each time a delivery is made the warehouse is restocked completely. The total demand during a time interval $(0, t]$ has the compound Poisson distribution (17), a negative demand indicating returned material. The demand is met "if physically possible," and moreover, returned material is accepted without limit. Show that the probability that the warehouse will not become empty between one delivery and the next is given by $\sum_{0}^{\infty} a_n P_n(c-)$, where

$$a_n = \int_0^\infty e^{-\lambda u} \frac{(\lambda u)^n}{n!} \, dA(u) \quad (n \geq 0).$$

5. **A Continuous Time Model with Time Lag.** A warehouse has capacity c $(0 < c < \infty)$, the stored material being measured in discrete units. The total demand $\xi(t)$ during a time interval $(0, t]$ has a simple Poisson distribution with parameter λ, and this demand is met "if physically possible." Orders for m items are placed at epochs at which the accumulated demand equals $m, 2m, 3m, \ldots$, but the delivery is made after a time lag T. Thus the inventory level at time t is given by

$$Z(t) = c + m \left[\frac{\xi(t-T)}{m} \right] - \xi(t),$$

where $[x]$ is the largest integer contained in x. Show that

$$\lim_{t \to \infty} P\{Z(t) = n\} = \frac{1}{m} \sum_{j=0}^{m-1} e^{-\lambda T} \frac{(\lambda T)^{c-n-j}}{(c-n-j)!}.$$

6. In the dam model of section 1, prove that (a) the limit d.f. $F(x)$ of Z_n as $n \to \infty$ exists, and (b) $F(x)$ satisfies the integral equation

$$F(x) = \int_{0-}^{c} dF(z) P(z; x), \tag{23}$$

where

$$P(z; x) = Q(z; x) + [1 - A(c - x -)][1 - B(c - z)],$$

$$Q(z; x) = \int_0^{c-z} dB(v)[1 - A(v + z - x -)],$$

and A and B are the d.f.'s of X_n and ξ_n respectively.

7. **Continuation.** Let Ω_{n+1} be the overflow and R_{n+1} the amount of water released from the dam at time $n+1$. Show that

$$E(\Omega_{n+1} + R_{n+1}) \to E(X_1). \tag{24}$$

8. **Continuation.** Let T be the time that the dam with an initial content z takes either to dry up or to overflow; thus

$$T = \min\{n: Z_{n-1} + X_n > c \text{ or } Z_{n-1} + X_n - \xi_n \le 0\}, \tag{25}$$

with $Z_0 = z$. Then the probability that the dam ever dries up before overflowing is given by

$$V(z) = P\{T < \infty, Z_{T-1} + X_T - \xi_T \le 0 | Z_0 = z\} \tag{26}$$

for $0 < z \le c$. Show that $V(z)$ satisfies the integral equation

$$V(z) = Q(z; 0) + \int_{0+}^{c} Q(z; dx) V(x), \tag{27}$$

with $V(z) = 0$ for $z \le 0$ and for $z > c$.

9. **The Case $c = \infty$.** Assume that the dam in section 1 has infinite capacity, and let $K(x)$ be the d.f. of the net input $X_n - \xi_n$. Prove the following:

   (i) If the limit d.f. $F(x)$ of Z_n as $n \to \infty$ exists, then it satisfies the integral equation

$$F(x) = \int_{0-}^{\infty} dF(z) K(x - z) \qquad (x \ge 0). \tag{28}$$

   (ii) The probability $V(z)$ that the dam with an initial content z (> 0) ever dries up satisfies the integral equation

$$V(z) = K(-z) + \int_{0+}^{\infty} V(x) K(dx - z) \qquad (z > 0) \tag{29}$$

   with $V(z) = 0$ for $z \le 0$.

10. **The Infinitely Deep Dam.** If the storage policy in the dam model of section 1 prescribes the release rule $f(Z_n + \eta_{n+1}, \xi_{n+1}) = \xi_{n+1}$, then the model describes an infinitely deep dam, with $-\infty < Z_n \le c$. Let $\bar{Z}_n = c - \xi_n - Z_n$ and

$$\bar{F}(z) = \lim_{n \to \infty} P\{\bar{Z}_n \ge z\}, \tag{30}$$

assuming this limit to exist. Show that $\bar{F}(z)$ satisfies the integral equation (29).

11. In P. A. P. Moran's model for the dam, the input X_{n+1} has d.f. $G(x)$, the demand $\xi_{n+1} \equiv m$ $(<c<\infty)$ and the prescribed release rule is $f(Z_n + \eta_{n+1}, \xi_{r+1}) = \min(Z_n + \eta_{n+1}, \xi_{n+1})$.

   (i) Prove that the limit d.f. $F(x)$ of Z_n as $n \to \infty$ satisfies the integral equation

$$F(x) = \int_{0-}^{c-m} dF(z) G(x - z + m) \quad \text{for } x < c - m, \tag{31}$$

with $F(x) = 1$ for $x \ge c - m$.

(ii) Let $T = \min\{n: Z_n = 0 \text{ or } Z_n = c - m\}$ and

$$V(z) = P\{T < \infty, Z_n = 0 | Z_0 = z\} \qquad (0 < z < c - m), \tag{32}$$

so that $V(z)$ is the probability that the dam with an initial content z ever dries up before overflowing. Prove that $V(z)$ satisfies the integral equation

$$V(z) = G(m - z) + \int_{0+}^{c-m-} V(x) G(dx - z + m), \tag{33}$$

with $V(z) = 0$ for $z \leq 0$ or $z \geq c - m$.

12. In the single-server queue of section 1, let $F(x)$ be the limit d.f. of W_n as $n \to \infty$ if it exists. Show that $F(x)$ satisfies the integral equation (28) with $K(x) = P\{v_n - u_n \leq x\}$.

13. In the model for insurance risk, let $F(t, x) = P\{T(x) > t\}$. Show that $F(t, x)$ satisfies the integro-differential equation

$$\frac{\partial F}{\partial t} - \beta \frac{\partial F}{\partial x} + \lambda F(t, x) = \lambda \int_{-\infty}^{x} F(t, x - y) \, dP(y),$$

with $F(0, x) = 1$ for $x \geq 0$.

14. Continuation. Let $\psi(x) = P\{T(x) < \infty\}$. Show that $\psi(x)$ satisfies the integro-differential equation

$$-\beta \psi'(x) + \lambda \psi(x) = \lambda [1 - P(x)] + \lambda \int_{-\infty}^{x} \psi(x - y) \, dP(y).$$

15. Continuation. Let $A(t)$ be the number of claims during an interval $(0, t]$, and

$$F_n(t; x) = P\{T(x) > t, A(t) = n\}.$$

Prove that

$$F_0(t, x) = e^{-\lambda t} P_0(x + \beta t),$$

$$F_n(t; x) = \int_{\tau=0}^{t^*} \int_{y=-\infty}^{x+\beta\tau} \lambda e^{-\lambda \tau} F_{n-1}(t - \tau; x + \beta\tau - y) \, dP(y) \, d\tau \qquad (n \geq 1),$$

where $t^* = t$ if $\beta \geq 0$, and $= \min(t, -x/\beta)$ if $\beta < 0$.

Selected Bibliography

1. Queueing Models

Benes, Václav E. (1963): *General Stochastic Processes in the Theory of Queues.* Addison-Wesley, Reading, Massachusetts.

Cohen, J. W. (1969): *The Single Server Queue.* North-Holland, Amsterdam.

Gnedenko, B. V. and Kovalenko, I. N. (1968): *Introduction to Queueing Theory.* Israel Program for Scientific Translations, Jerusalem.

Jaiswal, N. K. (1968): *Priority Queues*. Academic Press, New York.

Kendall, D. G. (1951): Some problems in the theory of queues. *J. Roy. Statist. Soc.* B **13**, 151–185.

Kendall, D. G. (1954): Stochastic processes occurring in the theory of queues and their analysis by the method of the imbedded Markov chain. *Ann. Math. Statist.* **24**, 338–354.

Kleinrock, Leonard (1975): *Queueing Systems, Volume I: Theory*. John Wiley, New York.

Kleinrock, Leonard (1976): *Queueing Systems, Volume II: Computer Applications*. John Wiley, New York.

Prabhu, N. U. (1965): *Queues and Inventories: A Study of Their Basic Stochastic Processes*. John Wiley, New York.

Syski, R. (1960): *Introduction to Congestion Theory in Telephone Systems*. Edinburgh: Oliver and Boyd, Edinburgh.

Takács, Lajos (1962): *Introduction to the Theory of Queues*. Oxford University Press, New York.

2. Inventories

Arrow, K., Karlin, S. and Scarf, H. (1958): *Studies in the Mathematical Theory of Inventory and Production*. Stanford University Press, Stanford, California.

Tijms, H. C. (1972): *Analysis of (s, S) Inventory Models*. Mathematics Centre Tracts No. 40. Mathematisch Centrum, Amsterdam.

3. Models for Dams

Hurst, H. E. (1951): Long term storage capacity of reservoirs. *Trans. Amer. Soc. Civ. Engrs.* **116**.

Hurst, H. E. (1956): *Methods of Using Long Term Storage in Reservoirs*. Inst. Civ. Engrs., London, Paper 6059.

Koopmans, Tjalling C. (1958): *Water Storage Policy in a Simplified Hydroelectric System*. Cowles Foundation Paper No. 115.

Little, John D. C. (1955): The use of storage water in a hydroelectric system. *Opns. Res.* **3**, 187–197.

Massé, P. (1946): *Les Reserves et la Regulation de l'Avenir dans la vie Economique*. Hermann, Paris.

Moran, P. A. P. (1959): *The Theory of Storage*. Methuen, London.

Prabhu, N. U. (1965): Op. cit.

4. Insurance Risk

Beard, R. E., Pentikäinen, T. and Personen, E. (1969): *Risk Theory*. Methuen, London.

Beekman, John A. (1974): *Two Stochastic Processes*. John Wiley, New York.

Buhlmann, H. (1970): *Mathematical Methods in Risk Theory.* Springer-Verlag, New York.

Seal, H. L. (1969): *Stochastic Theory of a Risk Business.* John Wiley, New York.

Seal, H. L. (1978): *Survival Probabilities: The Goal of Risk Theory.* John Wiley, New York.

PART I
THE SINGLE SERVER QUEUE

The close connection between random walks and queueing problems became evident from the work of D. V. Lindley, W. L. Smith, and F. Spitzer more than twenty years ago. The dominant feature of this unexpected connection is the Wiener–Hopf factorization, which has led to considerable simplification of queueing theory. We present here an account of the theory using random walk concepts and Wiener–Hopf techniques.

Chapter 1

The Queue G/G/1 and the Associated Random Walk

1 Orientation

We consider the single-server queueing system where successive customers arrive at the epochs $t_0(=0), t_1, t_2, \ldots$, and demand services times $v_1, v_2, \ldots$. The inter-arrival times are then given by $u_n = t_n - t_{n-1}$ $(n \geq 1)$. Let $X_k = v_k - u_k$ $(k \geq 1)$, and $S_0 \equiv 0$, $S_n = X_1 + X_2 + \cdots + X_n$ $(n \geq 1)$. We assume that the X_k are mutually independent random variables with a common distribution; the basic process underlying this queueing model is the random walk $\{S_n\}$. To see this, let W_n be the waiting time of the nth customer and I_n the idle period (if any) that just terminates upon the arrival of this customer. Then clearly for $n \geq 0$

$$W_{n+1} = \max(0, X_{n+1} + W_n), \qquad I_{n+1} = -\min(0, X_{n+1} + W_n). \qquad (1)$$

The total idle period up to the time of the nth arrival is given by

$$\mathscr{I}_0 = 0, \qquad \mathscr{I}_n = I_1 + I_2 + \cdots + I_n \qquad (n \geq 1). \qquad (2)$$

Now consider the sample sequence $\{W_n, n \geq 0\}$ whose first ten elements are given by

$$A = \{W_0 = 0, W_1 > 0, W_2 > 0, W_3 = 0, W_4 > 0,$$
$$W_5 > 0, W_6 > 0, W_7 = 0, W_8 > 0, W_9 > 0\}.$$

Using (1) and (2) we find that

$$W_1 = \max(0, X_1) = X_1 = S_1 > 0, \qquad I_1 = 0;$$
$$W_2 = \max(0, X_2 + X_1) = X_2 + X_1 = S_2 > 0, \qquad I_2 = 0;$$
$$W_3 = \max(0, X_3 + X_2 + X_1) = 0, \qquad I_3 = -S_3 \geq 0;$$

$$W_4 = \max(0, X_4) = X_4 = S_4 - S_3 > 0, \qquad I_4 = 0;$$
$$W_5 = \max(0, X_5 + X_4) = X_5 + X_4 = S_5 - S_3 > 0, \qquad I_5 = 0;$$
$$W_6 = \max(0, X_6 + S_5 - S_3) = X_6 + S_5 - S_3 = S_6 - S_3 > 0, \qquad I_6 = 0;$$
$$W_7 = \max(0, X_7 + S_6 - S_3) = 0, \qquad I_7 = S_3 - S_7 \geq 0;$$
$$W_8 = \max(0, X_8) = X_8 = S_8 - S_7 > 0, \qquad I_8 = 0;$$
$$W_9 = \max(0, X_9 + S_8 - S_7) = X_9 + S_8 - S_7 = S_9 - S_7 > 0, \qquad I_9 = 0.$$

Therefore we can write A as

$$A = \{S_0 = 0, S_1 > 0, S_2 > 0, S_3 \leq 0, S_4 > S_3,$$
$$S_5 > S_3, S_6 > S_3, S_7 \leq S_3, S_8 > S_7, S_9 > S_7\}.$$

Conversely, this sequence of partial sums S_n will lead us to the original sequence of W_n. The above results concerning W_n, I_n, and S_n are displayed in the following table:

Table 1

n	0	1	2	3	4	5	6	7	8	9
W_n	0	S_1	S_2	0	$S_4 - S_3$	$S_5 - S_3$	$S_6 - S_3$	0	$S_8 - S_7$	$S_9 - S_7$
I_n	0	0	0	$-S_3$	$-S_3$	$-S_3$	$-S_3$	$-S_7$	$-S_7$	$-S_7$

A close look at the above calculations motivates the introduction of the random variables $\{\bar{N}_k, k \geq 0\}$, where[1]

$$\bar{N}_0 \equiv 0,$$
$$\bar{N}_1 = \min\{n > 0 : S_n \leq 0\}, \tag{3}$$
$$\bar{N}_k = \min\{n > \bar{N}_{k-1} : S_n \leq S_{\bar{N}_{k-1}}\} \qquad (k \geq 2).$$

Let $\bar{Z}_k = S_{\bar{N}_k} - S_{\bar{N}_{k-1}}$ $(k \geq 1)$. For the sample sequence A we find that

$$\bar{N}_1 = 3, \qquad \bar{N}_2 = 7, \qquad \bar{Z}_1 = S_3, \qquad \bar{Z}_2 = S_7 - S_3.$$

Here during the first two busy periods $\bar{N}_1 = 3$ and $\bar{N}_2 - \bar{N}_1 = 4$ customers are served respectively, and these busy periods are followed by idle periods whose durations are given by $-\bar{Z}_1$ and $-\bar{Z}_2$. The durations of the first two busy periods are given by

$$B_1 = v_1 + v_2 + v_3, \qquad B_2 = v_4 + v_5 + v_6 + v_7.$$

It is thus obvious that the variables (3) contain a surprisingly rich amount of information concerning our queueing process.

---

[1] We use the convention that the minimum of an empty set is $+\infty$.

Let us also define the random variables $\{N_k, k \geq 0\}$, as follows:

$$N_0 \equiv 0,$$
$$N_1 = \min\{n : S_n > 0\}, \qquad (4)$$
$$N_k = \min\{n : S_n > S_{N_{k-1}}\} \qquad (k \geq 2).$$

Also, let $Z_k = S_{N_k} - S_{N_{k-1}}$ ($k \geq 1$). The significance of this second sequence is not immediately obvious, but we will need it to derive various distributions of interest to us.

The random variable N_k is called the kth ascending ladder epoch and S_{N_k} the corresponding ladder height. Similarly, $\bar{N}_k$ and $S_{\bar{N}_k}$ are called the kth descending[2] ladder epoch and height. We shall speak of (N_k, S_{N_k}) and $(\bar{N}_k, S_{\bar{N}_k})$ as the kth ascending and descending *ladder points* of the random walk $\{S_n\}$. These two ladder processes determine the recurrence properties of $\{S_n\}$. In sections 2–4 we develop the basic results concerning ladder processes arising from a general one-dimensional random walk.

2 Ladder Processes

Let $\{X_k, k \geq 1\}$ be a sequence of independent random variables with a common d.f.

$$K(x) = P\{X_n \leq x\} \qquad (-\infty < x < \infty). \qquad (5)$$

We ignore the trivial case where $X_k = 0$ with probability one. Let $S_0 \equiv 0$, $S_n = X_1 + X_2 + \cdots + X_n$ ($n \geq 1$); the sequence of partial sums $\{S_n\}$ defines a random walk induced by $K(x)$. For this random walk we define the two sequences of random variables $\{N_k\}$ and $\{\bar{N}_k\}$ as in the last section. For convenience let us denote $N_1 = N$ and $\bar{N}_1 = \bar{N}$. For the joint distribution of (N, S_N) we write

$$\begin{aligned} f_n(x) &= P\{N = n, S_N \leq x\} \\ &= P\{S_1 \leq 0, S_2 \leq 0, \ldots, S_{n-1} \leq 0, 0 < S_n \leq x\}. \end{aligned} \qquad (6)$$

This distribution will be called proper if

$$P\{N < \infty, S_N < \infty\} = \sum_1^\infty f_n(\infty) = 1, \qquad (7)$$

and otherwise defective. Similarly, let

$$\begin{aligned} g_n(x) &= P\{\bar{N} = n, S_{\bar{N}} \leq x\} \\ &= P\{S_1 > 0, S_2 > 0, \ldots, S_{n-1} > 0, S_n \leq x \leq 0\} \end{aligned} \qquad (8)$$

---
[2] On account of the weaker inequalities in (3), $\bar{N}_k$ are called *weak* ladder epochs, in contrast to N_k which are *strong* ladder epochs. However, we shall ignore this distinction here.

be the joint distribution of $(\bar{N}, S_{\bar{N}})$; this distribution may be proper or defective.

Transforms of the two distributions (6) and (8) will be derived in the next chapter. Here we are interested in the following important result.

Theorem 1 (Wiener–Hopf Factorization). *For $0 < z < 1$, ω real and $i = \sqrt{-1}$ we have*

$$1 - zE(e^{i\omega X_n}) = [1 - E(z^N e^{i\omega S_N})][1 - E(z^{\bar{N}} e^{i\omega S_{\bar{N}}})], \qquad (9)$$

the factorization being unique among factors of this type.

The proof of this theorem will be postponed to the next chapter. As an immediate consequence of (9) we have the following.

Theorem 2

(i) *The random variables N, $\bar{N}$ cannot be both defective.*
(ii) *If N, $\bar{N}$ are both proper, then $E(N) = E(\bar{N}) = \infty$.*
(iii) *If only one (say N) is proper, then $E(N) < \infty$.*

PROOF. (i) Setting $\omega = 0$ in (9) we obtain the identity

$$1 - z = [1 - E(z^N)][1 - E(z^{\bar{N}})] \qquad (10)$$

for $0 < z < 1$. Letting $z \to 1$ we find that

$$0 = [1 - P\{N < \infty\}][1 - P\{\bar{N} < \infty\}],$$

so at least one factor on the right side must vanish.

(ii) If N, $\bar{N}$ are both proper, then writing (10) as

$$[1 - E(z^{\bar{N}})] \cdot \frac{1 - E(z^N)}{1 - z} = 1$$

and letting $z \to 1$ we obtain $0 \cdot E(N) = 1$, which gives $E(N) = \infty$. Similarly $E(\bar{N}) = \infty$.

(iii) If N is proper and $\bar{N}$ defective the last argument shows that $E(N) = (1 - \bar{p})^{-1}$, where $\bar{p} = P\{\bar{N} < \infty\} < 1$. □

Once a ladder point is reached, the random walk starts from scratch in the sense that given (N_1, S_{N_1}) the random variables $S_n - S_{N_1}$ ($n > N_1$) depend only on X_k ($N_1 < k \leq n$) but not on X_k ($k \leq N_1$). It follows that the variables $(N_k - N_{k-1}, S_{N_k} - S_{N_{k-1}})$ ($k \geq 1$) form a renewal process in two dimensions. In other words these pairs of random variables are independent and have the same distribution as (N, S_N).

Now the sequence $\{S_{N_k}, k \geq 1\}$ is an increasing one and indicates the drift of the process to $+\infty$. If the distribution of (N, S_N) is defective, it is clear that there is a last index k such that $N_k < \infty$, but $N_{k+1} = \infty$, or

$$S_{N_k} < \infty, \quad S_n \leq S_{N_k} \text{ for all } n > N_k.$$

In this case the random walk attains a finite maximum, and then drifts to $-\infty$. A similar conclusion is reached when we consider the two-dimensional renewal process corresponding to the descending ladder points. These two ladder processes determine the behavior of the random walk as stated in the following theorem. For a proof see Feller [(1971), pp. 394–398].

Theorem 3. *The behavior of the random walk* $\{S_n\}$ *is related to the nature of the associated ladder processes in the following manner:*

(N, S_N)	$(\bar{N}, S_{\bar{N}})$	Type of random walk
Proper	proper	oscillating
Proper	defective	drifts to $+\infty$
Defective	proper	drifts to $-\infty$

3 Two Renewal Functions

We now investigate two functions related to the ladder processes described in the last section. First let

$$u_n(x) = P\{S_n > S_m \ (0 \leq m \leq n-1), S_n \leq x\} \quad (n \geq 1, x > 0), \quad (11)$$

$$\begin{aligned} u_0(x) &= 0 \quad \text{for } x < 0, \\ &= 1 \quad \text{for } x \geq 0. \end{aligned} \quad (12)$$

Note that unlike $f_n(x)$, $u_n(x)$ does not define a probability distribution; however we shall prove that the series

$$u(x) = \sum_0^\infty u_n(x) \quad (13)$$

converges for finite positive values of x. We also define

$$v_n(x) = P\{S_n \leq S_m \ (0 \leq m \leq n-1), S_n \geq x\} \quad (n \geq 1, x \leq 0), \quad (14)$$

$$\begin{aligned} v_0(x) &= 1 \quad \text{for } x \leq 0, \\ &= 0 \quad \text{for } x > 0, \end{aligned} \quad (15)$$

and

$$v(x) = \sum_0^\infty v_n(x), \quad (16)$$

where the series converges for finite negative x. These results are stated in the following theorem.

Theorem 4. *Let $u(x)$ and $v(x)$ be the two functions defined above. Then*

$$u(x) = 1 + \text{expected number of ascending ladder points in the interval } (0, x] \qquad (0 < x < \infty), \tag{17}$$

$$v(x) = 1 + \text{expected number of descending ladder points in the interval } [x, 0) \qquad (-\infty < x \leq 0), \tag{18}$$

and these two renewal functions are finite for values of x indicated above.

PROOF. The event $\{S_n > S_m \ (0 \leq m \leq n-1)\}$ occurs if and only if n is an ascending ladder epoch. Therefore

$$u_n(x) = P\{N_k = n, S_{N_k} \leq x \text{ for some } k \geq 1\}$$
$$= \sum_{k=1}^{\infty} P\{N_k = n, S_{N_k} \leq x\} \tag{19}$$

and

$$u(x) = 1 + \sum_{k=1}^{\infty} P\{S_{N_k} \leq x\}, \tag{20}$$

where the random variables S_{N_k} are the partial sums of the renewal sequence $\{Z_k\}$. The last sum therefore represents the renewal function of this sequence, that is, the expected number of renewals in the interval $(0, x]$. From renewal theory this function is known to be finite for finite positive x. Similarly $v(x)$ is finite for finite negative x. □

4 Maximum and Minimum

Let us consider the random variables

$$M_n = \max(0, S_1, S_2, \ldots, S_n), \qquad m_n = \min(0, S_1, S_2, \ldots, S_n) \qquad (n \geq 0). \tag{21}$$

Clearly $M_n \geq 0$, $m_n \leq 0$ with probability one. Also, the sequence $\{M_n\}$ is nondecreasing, while $\{m_n\}$ is nonincreasing. The intuitive arguments used in section 2 indicate that when the distribution of (N, S_N) is defective $M_n \to M$ as $n \to \infty$, where M is a random variable which is finite with probability one. Obviously a similar statement holds for m_n. In the following we derive the distributions of M_n and m_n. We first observe an important fact.

Lemma 1. *The joint distribution of $(M_n, M_n - S_n)$ is identical with that of $(S_n - m_n, -m_n)$.*

4 Maximum and Minimum

PROOF. The probability $P\{M_n \leq x, M_n - S_n \leq y\}$ is invariant under the permutation
$$(X_1, X_2, \ldots, X_n) \to (X_n, X_{n-1}, \ldots, X_1),$$
which results in the permutation of partial sums
$$(S_1, S_2, \ldots, S_n) \to (S'_1, S'_2, \ldots, S'_n),$$
with $S'_r = X_n + X_{n-1} + \cdots + X_{n-r+1} = S_n - S_{n-r}$. Therefore

$$P\{M_n \leq x, M_n - S_n \leq y\} = P\left\{\max_{0 \leq r \leq n} S_r \leq x, \max_{0 \leq r \leq n} (S_r - S_n) \leq y\right\}$$

$$= P\left\{\max_{0 \leq r \leq n} (S_n - S_{n-r}) \leq x, \max_{0 \leq r \leq n} (-S_{n-r}) \leq y\right\}$$

$$= P\{S_n - m_n \leq x, -m_n \leq y\},$$

as required. □

Theorem 5. *We have*

$$P\{M_n \leq x, M_n - S_n \leq y\} = P\{S_n - m_n \leq x, m_n \geq -y\}$$

$$= \sum_{m=0}^{n} u_m(x) v_{n-m}(-y) \qquad (n \geq 0, x \geq 0, y \geq 0).$$
(22)

PROOF. Let $N(n) = \max\{k: N_k \leq n\}$, so that $N(n)$ is the number of ascending ladder epochs in the time interval $(0, n]$. Then

$$P\{M_n \leq x, M_n - S_n \leq y\}$$

$$= \sum_{k=0}^{n} P\{N(n) = k, M_n \leq x, M_n - S_n \leq y\}$$

$$= \sum_{k=0}^{n} \sum_{m=k}^{n} P\{N_k = m, N_{k+1} > n, S_{N_k} \leq x, S_{N_k} - S_n \leq y\}$$

$$- \sum_{k=0}^{n} \sum_{m=k}^{n} \int_{0-}^{x} P\{N_k = m, S_{N_k} \in dz\}$$

$$\times P\{N_{k+1} > n, S_{N_k} - S_n \leq y | N_k = m, S_{N_k} = z\}.$$

Now
$$P\{N_{k+1} > n, S_{N_k} - S_n \leq y | N_k = m, S_{N_k} = z\}$$
$$= P\{N_{k+1} - N_k > n - m, S_n - S_{N_k} \geq -y | N_k = m, S_{N_k} = z\}$$
$$= P\{N_1 > n - m, S_{n-m} \geq -y\},$$
since as already observed, $(N_{k+1} - N_k, S_n - S_{N_k})$ is independent of the ladder point (N_k, S_{N_k}) and has the same distribution as (N_1, S_{n-N_k}).

Proceeding as in the proof of Lemma 1 we find that this last probability equals

$$P\{S_r \leq 0 \ (0 \leq r \leq n - m), S_{n-m} \geq -y\}$$
$$= P\{S_{n-m} \leq S_r \ (0 \leq r \leq n - m), S_{n-m} \geq -y\} \qquad (23)$$
$$= v_{n-m}(-y).$$

Collecting all of our results we obtain

$$P\{M_n \leq x, M_n - S_n \leq y\} = \sum_{m=0}^{n} \sum_{k=0}^{m} P\{N_k = m, S_{N_k} \leq x\} v_{n-m}(-y)$$
$$= \sum_{m=0}^{n} u_m(x) v_{n-m}(-y),$$

where we have used (19). In view of Lemma 1 the proof is thus complete. □

Theorem 6. *For the distributions of M_n and m_n we have*

$$P\{M_n \leq x\} = \sum_{0}^{n} u_m(x) v_{n-m}(-\infty) \qquad (n \geq 0, x \geq 0), \qquad (24)$$

$$P\{m_n \geq -y\} = \sum_{0}^{n} u_m(\infty) v_{n-m}(-y) \qquad (n \geq 0, y \geq 0). \qquad (25)$$

The limit distribution of M_n as $n \to \infty$ is proper iff $p < 1$, while that of m_n is proper iff $\bar{p} < 1$. These are given by

$$\lim_{n \to \infty} P\{M_n \leq x\} = (1 - p)u(x) \qquad (x \geq 0) \qquad (26)$$

$$\lim_{n \to \infty} P\{m_n \geq -y\} = (1 - \bar{p})v(-y) \qquad (y \geq 0). \qquad (27)$$

Here $p = P\{N < \infty\}$ and $\bar{p} = P\{\bar{N} < \infty\}$.

PROOF. The first two results follow from Theorem 5 if we let $y \to \infty$ and $x \to \infty$ respectively. To derive the limit distribution of M_n we note from (23) that

$$\lim_{n \to \infty} v_n(-\infty) = P\{N = \infty\} = 1 - p.$$

Moreover, if $p < 1$ then from (20) we find that

$$u(\infty) = 1 + \sum_{k=1}^{\infty} P\{N_k < \infty\} = \sum_{0}^{\infty} p^k = (1 - p)^{-1},$$

so that $(1 - p)u(x)$ is a proper d.f. Similar remarks apply to the limit distribution of m_n, and the proof is thus complete. □

Remark 1. In view of Theorem 2 we find from Theorem 6 that a random walk is

oscillating if $M_n \to \infty$, $m_n \to -\infty$,
drifts to $+\infty$ if $M_n \to +\infty$, $m_n \to m \ (> -\infty)$,
drifts to $-\infty$ if $M_n \to M \ (< \infty)$, $m_n \to -\infty$.

These results justify our intuitive arguments leading to Theorem 3 and supply a proof of it.

Remark 2. In the discussion so far no reference was made to the moments of the random variables X_k. Suppose now that the X_k have a finite mean α. As before we shall ignore the trivial case where $X_k = 0$ with probability one. For a better understanding of Theorems 2, 3, and 6 we state the following result due to Spitzer (1956).

Theorem 7. *The distribution of (N, S_N) is proper iff $\alpha \geq 0$, while the distribution of $(\overline{N}, S_{\overline{N}})$ is proper iff $\alpha \leq 0$.*

5 Application to the Queue G/G/1

We now apply the results of the last three sections to the single-server queue described in section 1. Let us recall that the random variables X_k in our case are defined by $X_k = v_k - u_k \ (k \geq 1)$. It is natural to assume that the X_k have a finite mean $\alpha = E(X_k)$. Let us also denote the variance of X_k as $\sigma^2 = E(X_k - \alpha)^2 \leq \infty$. Let W_n be the waiting time of the nth customer, and $\mathscr{I}_n$ the total idle period up to the time of this customer's arrival. The following results confirm our findings for the sample sequence A (table 1).

Theorem 8. *Let $W_0 \equiv 0$. We have then*

$$W_n = S_n + \mathscr{I}_n, \qquad \mathscr{I}_n = -m_n \qquad (n \geq 1). \tag{28}$$

PROOF. Since $W_0 = 0$ we obtain from (1) successively

$W_1 = \max(0, X_1)$,
$W_2 = \max(0, X_2 + W_1) = \max(0, X_2, X_2 + X_1)$,
$W_3 = \max(0, X_3 + W_2) = \max(0, X_3, X_3 + X_2, X_3 + X_2 + X_1)$,

and quite generally

$$W_n = \max(0, X_n + X_{n-1} + \cdots + X_{n-r+1} \ (1 \leq r \leq n))$$
$$= \max(S_n - S_{n-r} \ (0 \leq r \leq n))$$
$$= S_n + \max(-S_n, -S_{n-1}, \ldots, -S_1, 0) = S_n - m_n.$$

Again, using (1) we find that

$$I_n = \max(0, X_n + W_{n-1}) - (X_n + W_{n-1})$$
$$= W_n - W_{n-1} - X_n.$$

From this we obtain

$$\mathscr{I}_n = I_1 + I_2 + \cdots + I_n = W_n - S_n = -m_n.$$

The proof is thus complete. □

It is clear from the above theorem that the problem concerning the distribution of $(W_n, \mathscr{I}_n)$ is completely solved by Theorem 6. For completeness we state the relevant results below.

Theorem 9. (i) *If $W_0 \equiv 0$, then*

$$P\{W_n \leq x, \mathscr{I}_n \leq y\} = \sum_{m=0}^{n} u_m(x) v_{n-m}(-y) \qquad (n \geq 1, x \geq 0, y \geq 0). \quad (29)$$

(ii) *The limit d.f. of W_n is given by*

$$F(x) = (1-p) \sum_{0}^{\infty} u_n(x) \qquad (x \geq 0) \quad (30)$$

if $\alpha < 0$, while $F(x) \equiv 0$ if $\alpha \geq 0$.
(iii) *The limit d.f. of $\mathscr{I}_n$ is given by*

$$\bar{F}(y) = (1-\bar{p}) \sum_{0}^{\infty} v_n(-y) \qquad (y \geq 0) \quad (31)$$

if $\alpha > 0$, while $\bar{F}(x) \equiv 0$ if $\alpha \leq 0$.

The usual statement in the queueing literature is that the system is in statistical equilibrium if and only if $\alpha < 0$, in the sense that in this case W_n converges in distribution. It should be added, however, that if $\alpha < 0$, the total idle period $\mathscr{I}_n \to \infty$. The above results provide a better explanation of the nature of nonequilibrium. Thus if $\alpha < 0$, $W_n \to \infty$, while $\mathscr{I}_n$ converges, and if $\alpha = 0$ (the case that baffles intuition) both W_n and $\mathscr{I}_n \to \infty$.

It is possible to carry out a further investigation of nonequilibrium using the above results. We have already assumed that the basic random variables X_n have a finite mean. We now need a second assumption, namely that the X_n have a finite variance σ^2. For $\alpha > 0$ we have the following result.[3]

---

[3] Our assumptions amount to the statement that the X_n belong to the domain of attraction of the normal distribution. Heyde (1967) has obtained limit distributions for M_n in the case where the X_n belong to the domain of attraction of a stable distribution.

5 Application to the Queue G/G/1

Theorem 10. (i) *If $\alpha > 0$ and $\sigma^2 < \infty$, then*

$$\lim_{n \to \infty} P\left\{\frac{W_n - n\alpha}{\sigma\sqrt{n}} \leq x\right\} = N(x). \tag{32}$$

(ii) *If $\alpha < 0$ and $\sigma^2 < \infty$, then*

$$\lim_{n \to \infty} P\left\{\frac{\mathscr{I}_n + n\alpha}{\sigma\sqrt{n}} \leq x\right\} = N(x). \tag{33}$$

PROOF. (i) By Theorem 8 we have $W_n = S_n + \mathscr{I}_n$, which can be written as

$$\frac{W_n - n\alpha}{\sigma\sqrt{n}} = \frac{S_n - n\alpha}{\sigma\sqrt{n}} + \frac{\mathscr{I}_n}{\sigma\sqrt{n}}.$$

Here $\mathscr{I}_n$ has a limit distribution as $n \to \infty$ by Theorem 9, so $\mathscr{I}_n/\sqrt{n} \to 0$. The desired result follows from the central limit theorem for S_n. The proof of (ii) is similar. □

The case $\alpha = 0$ is somewhat more difficult. From Theorems 2 and 7 we know that in this case the ladder epochs $N, \bar{N}$ are both proper random variables with infinite means. However, it turns out that the ladder heights have finite means. Thus

$$E(Z) = \frac{\sigma}{2c}, \qquad E(\bar{Z}) = -c\sigma, \tag{34}$$

where

$$c = \frac{1}{\sqrt{2}} \exp\left\{\sum_{1}^{\infty} \frac{1}{n}\left[P\{S_n > 0\} - \frac{1}{2}\right]\right\} < \infty \tag{35}$$

(see Feller (1971), pp. 611–612). We need the following result.

Lemma 2. *Let $N(n)$ be the number of ascending ladder epochs of a random walk in the time interval $(0, n]$. If $\alpha = 0$ and $\sigma^2 < \infty$, then*

$$\lim_{n \to \infty} P\left\{\frac{N(n)}{2c\sqrt{n}} < x\right\} = N_+(x). \tag{36}$$

PROOF. We have

$$P\{N_1 > n\} \sim \frac{1}{c\sqrt{2n\pi}} \qquad (n \to \infty)$$

(see Feller (1971), p. 415). The Tauberian theorem therefore gives

$$\frac{1 - E(e^{-\theta N_1})}{\theta} \sim \frac{1}{c\sqrt{2\theta}} \qquad (\theta \to 0+).$$

Therefore

$$E(e^{-\theta 4c^2 N_k/k^2}) = \left[1 - \frac{\sqrt{2\theta}}{k} + O\left(\frac{1}{k}\right)\right]^k \to e^{-\sqrt{2\theta}}$$

as $k \to \infty$. Since $e^{-\sqrt{2\theta}}$ is the Laplace transform of the stable d.f. $G_{1/2}(x)$ it follows that as $k \to \infty$

$$P\left\{\frac{4c^2 N_k}{k^2} \leq x\right\} \to G_{1/2}(x). \tag{37}$$

Now we have

$$P\{N(n) < k\} = P\{N_k > n\},$$

which can be written as

$$P\left\{\frac{N(n)}{2c\sqrt{n}} < \frac{k}{2c\sqrt{n}}\right\} = P\left\{\frac{4c^2 N_k}{k^2} > \frac{4c^2 n}{k^2}\right\}. \tag{38}$$

In this let $n \to \infty$, $k \to \infty$ in such a way that $k/2c\sqrt{n} \to x > 0$ (fixed). Then by (37) the right side of (38) converges to

$$1 - G_{1/2}(x^{-2}) = 2N(x) - 1 = N_+(x)$$

and therefore

$$P\left\{\frac{N(n)}{2c\sqrt{n}} < x\right\} \to N_+(x),$$

as required. □

The lemma just proved leads to the following result, first proved by Erdos and Kac (1946) by other methods.

Theorem 11. *If $\alpha = 0$ and $\sigma^2 < \infty$, then*

$$\lim_{n \to \infty} P\left\{\frac{W_n}{\sigma\sqrt{n}} \leq x\right\} = N_+(x) \tag{39}$$

and

$$\lim_{n \to \infty} P\left\{\frac{\mathscr{I}_n}{\sigma\sqrt{n}} \leq x\right\} = N_+(x). \tag{40}$$

PROOF. From Theorem 8 and Lemma 1 we find that[4] $W_n \sim M_n$. Therefore it suffices to consider M_n. We have

$$M_n = Z_1 + Z_2 + \cdots + Z_{N(n)}, \tag{41}$$

---

[4] For two random variables X, Y we write $X \sim Y$ if they have the same distribution.

5 Application to the Queue G/G/1

where $Z_1, Z_2, \ldots$ are the successive ascending ladder steps. Therefore

$$\frac{M_n}{\sigma\sqrt{n}} = \frac{Z_1 + Z_2 + \cdots + Z_{N(n)}}{E(Z)N(n)} \cdot \frac{N(n)}{2c\sqrt{n}}. \tag{42}$$

Since $E(Z) = \sigma/2c$ by (34), the first factor on the right side of (44) tends to unity as $n \to \infty$ by the strong law of large numbers, while the second factor converges in distribution by Lemma 2. The result (39) follows immediately. The proof of (40) is similar. □

Duality. If the sequence $\{(u_k, v_k), k \geq 1\}$ describes a single server queueing system, then we define its dual system as the one described by the sequence $\{(v_k, u_k), k \geq 1\}$. If $\{S_n\}$ is the random walk associated with the given system, then that associated with the dual is the *reflected* random walk $\{-S_n\}$. When dealing with specific queueing systems some tedious calculations can be avoided by noting the following:

Theorem 12. *Let W_n, $\mathcal{I}_n$ denote respectively the nth customer's waiting time and the total idle period up to the time of his arrival in a given system. Let W'_n, $\mathcal{I}'_n$ denote the corresponding quantities in the dual system. Then we have*

$$(W'_n, \mathcal{I}'_n) \sim (\mathcal{I}_n, W_n). \tag{43}$$

PROOF. We have (with obvious notations)

$$W'_n = S'_n - m'_n = -\min(S'_r - S'_n) = -\min(S_n - S_r) = M_n - S_n,$$
$$\mathcal{I}'_n = -m'_n = -\min(S'_r) = -\min(-S_r) = M_n.$$

Therefore using Lemma 1 we find that

$$(W'_n, \mathcal{I}'_n) = (M_n - S_n, M_n) \sim (-m_n, S_n - m_n) = (\mathcal{I}_n, W_n),$$

as required. □

Theorem 13. *Suppose that the random walk associated with a given queueing system is induced by a continuous distribution, and let (N, S_N) be the first ascending ladder point of this random walk. Then if $\bar{N}'$ is the number of customers served during a busy period and I' the duration of the idle period that follows it in the dual system, we have*

$$(\bar{N}', I') \sim (N, S_N). \tag{44}$$

PROOF. Since $P\{S'_n = 0\}$ we have[5]

$$\bar{N}' = \min\{n: S'_n < 0\} \sim \min\{n: S_n > 0\} = N$$

and $I' = -S'_{\bar{N}'} \sim S_N$. □

---

[5] The distinction between strong and weak ladder epoch disappears as the distribution of X_k is continuous. See footnote 2.

6 The Queue M/M/1

As an application of the results of the preceding section we first consider the queue M/M/1 in which the inter-arrival times have the density $\lambda e^{-\lambda x}$, and the service times have the density $\mu e^{-\mu x}$ $(0 < \lambda < \infty, 0 < \mu < \infty)$. The traffic intensity is $\rho = \lambda \mu^{-1}$ $(0 < \rho < \infty)$. The random variables $X_k = v_k - u_k$ have the density $k(x)$ given by

$$k(x) = \frac{\lambda \mu}{\lambda + \mu} e^{\lambda x} \quad \text{for } x \le 0,$$

$$= \frac{\lambda \mu}{\lambda + \mu} e^{-\mu x} \quad \text{for } x \ge 0. \tag{45}$$

The c.f. of X_k is therefore given by

$$\phi(\omega) = \int_{-\infty}^{\infty} e^{i\omega x} k(x)\, dx = \frac{\lambda \mu}{(\lambda + i\omega)(\mu - i\omega)}. \tag{46}$$

We first obtain the distributions of the first ascending and descending ladder points (N, S_N) and $(\bar{N}, S_{\bar{N}})$.

Lemma 3. *For the random walk induced by the density* (45) *we have*

$$E(z^N e^{i\omega S_N}) = \frac{\lambda \xi(z)}{\mu - i\omega}, \qquad E(z^{\bar{N}} e^{i\omega S_{\bar{N}}}) = \frac{\lambda \xi(z)}{\lambda + i\omega}, \tag{47}$$

where $0 < z < 1$, ω *real, and*

$$\xi(z) = \frac{(\lambda + \mu) - \sqrt{(\lambda + \mu)^2 - 4\lambda\mu z}}{2\lambda}.$$

Furthermore,

$$p = P\{N < \infty, S_N < \infty\} = \min(1, \rho), \tag{48}$$

$$\bar{p} = P\{\bar{N} < \infty, S_{\bar{N}} > -\infty\} = \min(1, \rho^{-1}). \tag{49}$$

PROOF. We have

$$1 - z\phi(\omega) = \frac{(a - i\omega)(i\omega - b)}{(\mu - i\omega)(\lambda + i\omega)}, \tag{50}$$

where a, b are the roots of the quadratic equation (in $i\omega$) given by

$$(i\omega)^2 - i\omega(\mu - \lambda) - \lambda\mu(1 - z) = 0. \tag{51}$$

Our objective is to prove that $1 - z\phi(\omega)$ is of the form given by Theorem 1 (Wiener–Hopf factorization). In order to do this we write

$$\frac{(a - i\omega)(i\omega - b)}{(\mu - i\omega)(\lambda + i\omega)} = \left(1 - \frac{\mu - a}{\mu - i\omega}\right)\left(1 - \frac{\lambda + b\omega}{\lambda + i\omega}\right)$$

and verify whether the functions
$$\frac{\mu - a}{\mu - i\omega}, \quad \frac{\lambda + b}{\lambda + i\omega}$$
are transforms of the required type. In particular for $\omega = 0$ we must have
$$0 < 1 - \frac{a}{\mu} < 1 \quad \text{and} \quad 0 < 1 + \frac{b}{\lambda} < 1;$$
that is, $0 < a < \mu$ and $-\lambda < b < 0$. These conditions are satisfied if we take the roots of (51) to be
$$a = \frac{\mu - \lambda + \sqrt{(\mu - \lambda)^2 + 4\lambda\mu(1 - z)}}{2},$$
$$b = \frac{\mu - \lambda - \sqrt{(\mu - \lambda)^2 + 4\lambda\mu(1 - z)}}{2}$$
and this choice is unique. It turns out that $1 + b\lambda^{-1} = \xi(z)$ and $1 - a\mu^{-1} = \lambda\mu^{-1}\xi(z)$. By the uniqueness of the Wiener–Hopf factorization of $1 - z\phi(\omega)$ we obtain the results (47). The remaining results follow from the fact that as $z \to 1$, $\xi(z) \to \min(1, \rho^{-1})$. $\square$

It is clear from (47) that the random variables N, S_N are independent, and so are $\bar{N}$, $S_{\bar{N}}$. This latter fact deserves special attention in the queueing system and is stated below as a theorem. The limit distributions of the waiting time W_n and the idle time $\mathscr{I}_n$ can be obtained easily from this fact.

Theorem 14. *In the* M/M/1 *queue the number $\bar{N}$ of customers served during a busy period and the idle period I that follows it are independent; $\bar{N}$ has the p.g.f. $\xi(z)$, while I has the density $\lambda\rho e^{-\lambda x}$.*

PROOF. Since $I = -S_{\bar{N}}$ we obtain from (47)
$$E(z^{\bar{N}} e^{i\omega I}) = \frac{\lambda \xi(z)}{\lambda - i\omega}.$$
This gives $E(z^{\bar{N}}) = \xi(z)$ and $E(e^{i\omega I}) = \lambda\bar{\rho}(\lambda - i\omega)^{-1}$, where the last expression is the c.f. of the density $\lambda\bar{\rho} e^{-\lambda x}$. $\square$

Theorem 15. *In the queue* M/M/1 *the limit d.f. of the nth customer's waiting time is given by*
$$F(x) = 1 - \rho e^{-(\mu - \lambda)x} \quad (\rho < 1) \tag{52}$$
and the limit d.f. of the total idle period up to the time of the nth arrival is given by
$$\bar{F}(y) = 1 - \rho^{-1} e^{-(\lambda - \mu)x} \quad (\rho > 1). \tag{53}$$

PROOF. It suffices to prove (53), the proof of (52) being similar. From Theorem 9 we find the $\bar{F}(y) = (1 - \bar{p})v(-y)$ for $\bar{p} = \rho^{-1} < 1$. To calculate $v(-y)$ we note from Theorem 14 that $-S_{\bar{N}_k}$ has the d.f. $p^{-k}G_k(x)$ where

$$G_k(x) = 0 \quad \text{for } x \leq 0$$
$$= \int_0^x e^{-\lambda y} \lambda^k \frac{y^{k-1}}{(k-1)!} \, dy \quad \text{for } x \geq 0.$$

Therefore

$$v(-y) = 1 + \sum_{k=1}^{\infty} P\{S_{\bar{N}_k} \geq -y\}$$

$$= 1 + \sum_{k=1}^{\infty} \bar{p}^k G_k(y) = 1 + \sum_{k=1}^{\infty} \bar{p}^k \int_0^y e^{-\lambda x} \lambda^k \frac{x^{k-1}}{(k-1)!} \, dx$$

$$= 1 + \lambda \bar{p} \int_0^y e^{-(\lambda - \lambda \bar{p})x} \, dx$$

$$= (1 - \bar{p})^{-1}[1 - \bar{p} e^{-(\lambda - \mu)y}],$$

and the result (53) follows. □

7 The Queues G/M/1 and M/G/1

7.1 The Queue G/M/1

Let us consider the queue where the inter-arrival times u_k have the d.f. $H(x)$ with mean b $(0 < b < \infty)$, and the service times have the density $\lambda e^{-\lambda x}$ $(0 < \lambda < \infty)$. The traffic intensity is given by $\rho_2 = (\lambda b)^{-1}$. Let the Laplace transform of H be denoted by

$$\psi(\theta) = \int_0^\infty e^{-\theta x} \, dH(x) \qquad (\theta > 0). \tag{54}$$

The d.f. of $X_k = v_k - u_k$ is then given by

$$K(x) = \iint_{\{(u,v):\, u \geq 0,\, v \geq 0,\, v - u \leq x\}} \lambda e^{-\lambda v} \, dH(u)$$

$$= \int_{\max(0,\,-x)}^\infty dH(u)[1 - e^{-\lambda(u+x)}]$$

$$= \int_{-x}^\infty dH(u)[1 - e^{-\lambda(u+x)}] \quad \text{for } x \leq 0,$$

$$= 1 - c e^{-\lambda x} \quad \text{for } x \geq 0,$$

7 The Queues G/M/1 and M/G/1

where $c = \psi(\lambda)$. This distribution has the *partial lack of memory* property in the sense that

$$P\{X_k \leq y \mid X_k > x\} = 1 - e^{-\lambda(y-x)} \qquad (y > x \geq 0). \tag{55}$$

Lemma 4. *For the random walk induced by the d.f. $K(x)$ we have*

$$E[z^N e^{i\omega S_N}] = \frac{\lambda \xi}{\lambda - i\omega}, \qquad E(z^{\bar{N}} e^{i\omega S_{\bar{N}}}) = \frac{\lambda \xi - \lambda z \phi_1(-\omega)}{\lambda \xi - \lambda + i\omega}, \tag{56}$$

where $0 < z < 1$, ω real, ϕ_1 is the c.f. of the d.f. H, and $\xi = \xi(z)$ is the unique continuous solution of the equation

$$\xi = z\psi(\lambda - \lambda \xi) \tag{57}$$

in the interval $0 < z < 1$.

PROOF. We have

$$f_n(x) = P\{N = n, S_N \leq x\}$$
$$= P\{S_1 \leq 0, S_2 \leq 0, \ldots, S_{n-1} \leq 0, 0 < S_n \leq x\}$$
$$= \int_{-\infty}^{0} P\{S_1 \leq 0, \ldots, S_{n-2} \leq 0, S_{n-1} \in dy, S_n > 0\}$$
$$\cdot P\{S_n \leq x \mid S_{n-1} = y, S_n > 0\}.$$

Now for $x > 0$, $y \leq 0$ we have

$$P\{S_n \leq x \mid S_{n-1} = y, S_n > 0\} = P\{X_n \leq x - y \mid S_{n-1} = y, X_n > -y\}$$
$$= P\{X_n \leq x - y \mid X_n > -y\}$$

since X_n is independent of S_{n-1}. Using the lack of memory property (55) we find that this last probability equals $1 - e^{-\lambda x}$. Therefore

$$f_n(x) = P\{S_1 \leq 0, \ldots, S_{n-1} \leq 0, S_n > 0\}(1 - e^{-\lambda x})$$
$$= P\{N_1 = n\}(1 - e^{-\lambda x}) = f_n(\infty)(1 - e^{-\lambda x}). \tag{58}$$

Let us write $\xi(z) = \sum_1^\infty f_n(\infty) z^n$. Then

$$E(z^N e^{i\omega S_N}) = \sum_1^\infty z^n \int_0^\infty e^{i\omega x} f_n(dx) = \frac{\lambda \xi}{\lambda - i\omega}. \tag{59}$$

It remains to determine ξ and also to evaluate $\bar{\chi}(z, \omega) = E(z^{\bar{N}} e^{i\omega S_{\bar{N}}})$. In order to do this we note that the c.f. of X_k is given by

$$E(e^{i\omega X_k}) = \frac{\lambda}{\lambda - i\omega} \phi_1(-\omega).$$

The Wiener–Hopf factorization in the present case is given by

$$1 - z \frac{\lambda}{\lambda - i\omega} \phi_1(-\omega) = \left(1 - \frac{\lambda \xi}{\lambda - i\omega}\right)(1 - \bar{\chi}).$$

This gives

$$\bar{X}(z, \omega) = \frac{-\lambda\xi + c\lambda z + z(\lambda - i\omega)K_1^*(\omega)}{\lambda - \lambda\xi - i\omega} \quad (60)$$

for $0 < z < 1$ and real ω. Since $\phi_1(-\omega)$ is bounded and analytic for $I_m(\omega) < 0$, it is clear that we can use analytic extension to claim (60) to be valid for $I_m(\omega) < 0$. We notice that the denominator in the last expression vanishes at $\omega = \omega_0 = -i\lambda(1-\xi)$. Since $I_m(\omega_0) < 0$, the numerator should also vanish at $\omega = \omega_0$. This leads to the equation (57), since $\phi_1(i\theta) = \psi(\theta)$. It turns out that the expression $\psi(\lambda - \lambda\xi)$ in the equation (57) is a p.g.f., and therefore the existence and uniqueness of its solution follows from Theorem A1. The lemma is completely proved. □

From Theorem A1 we find that as $z \to 1$, $\xi(z) \to p$, where p is the least positive root of the equation

$$p = \psi(\lambda - \lambda p), \quad (61)$$

and $p < 1$ iff $\rho_2 < 1$.

Theorem 16. *The following results hold for the queue G/M/1.*
(i) *The number of customers served during a busy period has the p.g.f.*

$$E(z^{\bar{N}}) = \frac{z - \xi}{1 - \xi}. \quad (62)$$

(ii) *The idle period has the density given by*

$$\begin{aligned} h_p(x) &= 0 & \text{for } x \leq 0, \\ &= \lambda \int_x^\infty e^{-(\lambda - \lambda p)(y-x)} \, dH(y) & \text{for } x \geq 0. \end{aligned} \quad (63)$$

PROOF. The joint distribution of the number $\bar{N}$ of customers served during a busy period and the duration of the idle period $I = -S_{\bar{N}}$ that follows the busy period has the transform $E(z^{\bar{N}} e^{i\omega S_{\bar{N}}})$ given by (56). In this putting $\omega = 0$ we obtain (62), and letting $z \to 1$ and putting $\omega = -i\theta$ we obtain

$$E(e^{-\theta I}) = \lambda \frac{p - \psi(\theta)}{\theta - \lambda + \lambda p}, \quad (64)$$

where $p = P\{N < \infty, S_N < \infty\} \leq 1$. It is easily seen that the right side of (64) is the transform of the density (63). The proof is thus complete. □

Theorem 17. *In the queue G/M/1 the limit d.f. of the nth customer's waiting time is given by*

$$F(x) = 1 - p e^{-(\lambda - \lambda p)x} \quad (\rho_2 < 1), \quad (65)$$

and the limit d.f. of the total idle period up to the time of the nth arrival is given by

$$\bar{F}(y) = (1 - \rho_2^{-1}) \sum_{k=0}^{\infty} h_1^{(k)}(y) \qquad (\rho_2 > 1), \qquad (66)$$

where $h_1^{(1)}(y) \equiv h_1(y)$, that is,

$$h_1^{(1)}(y) = 0 \qquad \text{for } y \leq 0,$$
$$= \lambda \int_0^y [1 - H(u)] \, du \qquad \text{for } y \geq 0, \qquad (67)$$

$h_1^{(k)}(y)$ is the k-fold convolution of $h_1^{(1)}(y)$ with itself $(k \geq 2)$ and $h_1^{(0)}(y) = 0$ for $y < 0$ and $= 1$ for $y \geq 0$.

PROOF. The desired results follow from an argument similar to that used in Theorem 15, since the ascending ladder height S_N has the density $\lambda p e^{-\lambda x}$ with $p < 1$ for $\rho_2 < 1$, while the idle period has the density $h_1^{(1)}(y)$ for $\rho_2 > 1$. □

7.2 The Queue M/G/1

Next let us consider the queue where the customers arrive in a Poisson process at a rate λ $(0 < \lambda < \infty)$, and the service times have the d.f. $H(x)$ with mean b $(0 < b < \infty)$. The traffic intensity is $\rho_1 = \lambda b$. This queue is the dual of G/M/1, so Theorems 13 and 14 hold. It is useful to note that $\rho_1 \rho_2 = 1$.

Theorem 18. *The following results hold for the queue* M/G/1.

(i) *The number of customers served during a busy period has the p.g.f. $\xi(z)$, and the idle period that follows it has density $\lambda p e^{-\lambda x}$.*
(ii) *The limit d.f. of the nth customer's waiting time is given by*

$$F(x) = (1 - \rho_1) \sum_0^{\infty} h_1^{(k)}(x) \qquad (\rho_1 < 1). \qquad (68)$$

(iii) *The limit d.f. of the total idle period up to the time of the nth arrival is given by*

$$\bar{F}(x) = 1 - p e^{-(\lambda - \lambda p)x} \qquad (\rho_1 > 1). \qquad (69)$$

PROOF. Using Theorem 13 we see from Lemma 4 that the number of customers served during a busy period has the p.g.f. $\xi(z)$, and the idle period has the c.f. $\lambda p(\lambda - i\omega)^{-1}$. The remaining results follow from Theorem 17 on account of Theorem 12. The proof is thus complete. □

Remark. The Laplace transform of the limit distribution of the waiting time is given by the so-called Pollaczek–Khintchine formula

$$\int_{0-}^{\infty} e^{-\theta x}\, dF(x) = \frac{(1-\rho_1)\theta}{\theta - \lambda + \lambda\psi(\theta)} \qquad (\theta > 0). \tag{70}$$

Beneš (1957) inverted this transform and obtained the result (68). Kendall (1957) carried out a similar inversion in storage theory. The appearance of the form (68) caused a mild surprise at that time. However we now know its interpretation in terms of ladder processes.

8 Application to Queue Length

Although our interest in ladder processes was motivated by the consideration of waiting times and idle periods in the general single-server queue, it turns out that these processes are also of importance to the study of queue length in some special systems. We illustrate this by considering the systems M/G/1 and G/M/1 described in the last section.

We first observe that the queue length process $Q(t)$ is not in general Markovian. However, some progress in the investigation of $Q(t)$ can be made if we can find a sequence of epochs $\{t_n, n \geq 0\}$ such that $t_0 < t_1 < t_2 < \cdots$ and $\{Q(t_n), n \geq 0\}$ is a Markov chain. The epochs t_n are then called *points of regeneration* of the process, and the Markov chain is said to be *imbedded* in it. It so happens that for the systems M/G/1 and G/M/1 we can find such sequences.

8.1 The Queue M/G/1

If τ_n denotes the epoch of departure of the nth customer ($n = 0, 1, 2, \ldots$; $\tau_0 = 0$), it is easy to see that $\tau_n + 0$ ($n \geq 0$) are points of regeneration of $Q(t)$. Let $Q_n = Q(\tau_n + 0)$ ($n \geq 0$). Also, let X_n be the number of arrivals during the service time of the customer leaving at τ_n; then the random variables X_n ($n = 1, 2, \ldots$) are independent and have the common distribution $\{k_j\}$, where

$$k_j = P\{X_n = j\} = \int_0^{\infty} e^{-\lambda t} \frac{(\lambda t)^j}{j!} H(dt) \qquad (j \geq 0). \tag{71}$$

We have

$$Q_{n+1} = \max(X_{n+1}, X_{n+1} - 1 + Q_n) \qquad (n \geq 0). \tag{72}$$

8.2 The Queue G/M/1

Let $t_0 = 0, t_1, t_2, \ldots$ be the epochs of arrival of successive customers in this system, and $Q_n = Q(t_n - 0)$. Here $t_n - 0$ $(n \geq 1)$ are points of regeneration of the queue length process. Let X_{n+1} be the number of customers *who can be served* during $[t_n, t_{n+1})$ if a sufficient number of customers were waiting at t_n. Thus

$$X_{n+1} = \max\{k: v_{n+1-Q_n} + v_{n+2-Q_n} + \cdots + v_{n+k-Q_n} \leq u_{n+1}\}.$$

The *actual* number of customers served during $[t_n, t_{n+1})$ is given by

$$D_{n+1} = \min(Q_n + 1, X_{n+1}), \tag{74}$$

and therefore

$$Q_{n+1} = Q_n + 1 - D_{n+1} = -\min(0, X_{n+1} - 1 - Q_n) \quad (n \geq 0). \tag{75}$$

Here the X_n are independent random variables with the common distribution (71).

The relations (72) and (75) indicate that the basic process underlying each of these queueing models is the random walk induced by the distribution of $X_n - 1$. Let us denote the p.g.f. of X_n by

$$K(z) = \sum_0^\infty k_j z^j \quad (0 < z < 1) \tag{76}$$

and assume that $0 < E(X_n) < \infty$. Also, let $\alpha = E(X_n) - 1$. Let $S_0 \equiv 0$, $S_n = X_1 + X_2 + \cdots + X_n - n$ $(n \geq 1)$. We define the descending ladder epochs $\{\bar{N}_k, k \geq 0\}$ by

$$\bar{N}_0 \equiv 0,$$
$$\bar{N}_1 = \min\{n: S_n < 0\}, \tag{77}$$
$$\bar{N}_k = \min\{n: S_n < S_{\bar{N}_{k-1}}\} \quad (k \geq 2),$$

and the ascending ladder epochs $\{N_k, k \geq 0\}$ by

$$N_0 \equiv 0,$$
$$N_1 = \min\{n > 0: S_n \geq 0\}, \tag{78}$$
$$N_k = \min\{n > N_{k-1}: S_n \geq S_{N_{k-1}}\} \quad (k \geq 2).$$

Also,[6] let

$$v_n(j) = P\{n \text{ is a descending ladder epoch, and } S_n = -j\}, \tag{79}$$
$$u_n(j) = P\{n \text{ is an ascending ladder epoch, and } S_n = j\}, \tag{80}$$

---

[6] Here we deal with weak ascending epochs and strong descending epochs. See footnote 1.

for $n \geq 1$, $j \geq 0$, and
$$v_0(i) = u_0(i) = \delta_{0i}, \qquad (81)$$
where $\delta_{0i} = 1$ if $i = 0$, and $= 0$ for $i \neq 0$. As usual we write N, $\bar{N}$ for N_1, $\bar{N}_1$.

Lemma 5. *For the random walk described above we have*
$$E(z^{\bar{N}}\theta^{S_{\bar{N}}}) = \theta^{-1}\xi, \qquad E(z^N \theta^{S_N}) = \frac{\xi - zK(\theta)}{\xi - \theta}, \qquad (82)$$
where $0 < z < 1$, $0 < \theta < 1$, and $\xi = \xi(z)$ is the unique root of the equation $\xi = zK(\xi)$ in the interval $0 < z < 1$. Furthermore,
$$V(z) = \sum_0^\infty v_n(i)z^n = \xi^i \qquad (i \geq 0) \qquad (83)$$
and
$$U(z, \theta) = \sum_0^\infty \sum_0^\infty u_n(j) z^n \theta^j = \frac{\theta - \xi}{\theta - zK(\theta)}. \qquad (84)$$

PROOF. Since the negative steps of the random walk are of magnitude -1 with probability one, it is clear that $S_{\bar{N}} \equiv -1$. Denoting the p.g.f. of $\bar{N}$ by $\xi(z)$ we have therefore
$$E(z^{\bar{N}}\theta^{S_{\bar{N}}}) = \theta^{-1} E(z^{\bar{N}}) = \theta^{-1}\xi(z).$$
It is also clear that $S_{\bar{N}_i} = -i$ $(i \geq 1)$, and so
$$v_n(i) = \sum_{k=1}^\infty P\{\bar{N}_k = n, S_{\bar{N}_k} = -i\} = P\{\bar{N}_i = n\}, \qquad (85)$$
from which the result (83) follows. To determine ξ we note that
$$v_n(1) = P\{S_r > S_n \ (1 \leq r \leq n-1), S_n = -1\}$$
$$= \sum_1^\infty P\{S_1 = i - 1\} P\{S_r > S_n \ (2 \leq r \leq n-1), S_n = -1 | S_1 = i - 1\}$$
$$= \sum_1^\infty k_i P\{S_r - S_1 > S_n - S_1 \ (2 \leq r \leq n-1), S_n - S_1 = -i | S_1 = i - 1\}$$
$$= \sum_1^\infty k_i P\{S_{r'} > S_{n-1} \ (1 \leq r' \leq n-2), S_{n-1} = -i\} = \sum_1^\infty k_i v_{n-1}(i).$$
Thus
$$v_n(1) = \sum_0^\infty k_i v_{n-1}(i) \qquad (n \geq 1); \qquad (86)$$
using (83) we obtain $\xi = zK(\xi)$. Uniqueness of the root follows from Theorem A1.

8 Application to Queue Length

It remains to prove the results concerning ascending ladder points. Using the fact that the required probability is invariant under the permutation

$$(X_1, X_2, \ldots, X_n) \to (X_n, X_{n-1}, \ldots, X_1),$$

we find that

$$\begin{aligned} P\{N = n, S_N = j\} &= P\{S_r < 0 \ (1 \leq r \leq n-1), S_n = j\} \\ &= P\{S_n - S_{n-r} < 0 \ (1 \leq r \leq n-1), S_n = j\} \\ &= P\{S_{r'} > S_n \ (1 \leq r' \leq n-1), S_n = j\}. \end{aligned}$$

Proceeding as for (86) we obtain

$$P\{N = n, S_N = j\} = \sum_{j+1}^{\infty} k_i v_{n-1}(i - j - 1) \qquad (n \geq 1, j \geq 0). \tag{87}$$

This yields the second result in (82). We also have

$$u_n(j) = \sum_{k=i}^{\infty} P\{N_k = n, S_{N_k} = j\},$$

so that

$$\begin{aligned} U(z, \theta) &= \sum_0^{\infty} E(z^{N_k} \theta^{S_{N_k}}) = \sum_0^{\infty} [E(z^N \theta^{S_N})]^k \\ &= [1 - E(z^N \theta^{S_N})]^{-1}, \end{aligned}$$

which simplifies to (84). The lemma is therefore completely proved. □

Lemma 5 is the discrete analogue of Lemma 4 and can be proved by using Wiener–Hopf factorization. However, the above proof is elementary and illustrates the power of probabilistic arguments.

We are now in a position to apply the above results to the queueing systems M/G/1 and G/M/1. In both cases the random variables X_n have the p.g.f. $K(z) = \psi(\lambda - \lambda z)$ and $E(X_n) = K'(1) = -\lambda \psi'(0)$. This gives $\alpha = \rho_1 - 1$ for M/G/1 and $\alpha = \rho_2^{-1} - 1$ for G/M/1. The equation $\xi = zK(\xi)$ reduces to (57). Theorem A1 gives $\xi(1) = 1$ or ζ according as $K'(1) \leq 1$ or $K'(1) > 1$. We define the sequences $\{v_n\}$ and $\{u_n\}$ as follows:

$$v_n = \sum_{i=1}^{\infty} v_n(i), \qquad u_n = \sum_{j=0}^{\infty} u_n(j) \qquad (n \geq 1) \tag{88}$$

$$v_0 = u_0 = 1. \tag{89}$$

Theorem 19. *For the queue* M/G/1 *with* $Q_0 = 0$ *we have the following results.*

(i) *The queue length* Q_n *at* $\tau_n + 0$ *is given by*

$$Q_n = S_n + \bar{N}(n), \tag{90}$$

where $\bar{N}(n)$ is the number of idle periods up to the nth departure, that is,
$$\bar{N}(n) = \min\{i: \bar{N}_i \geq n\}. \tag{91}$$

(ii) *The distribution of Q_n has the transform given by*
$$\sum_0^\infty z^n E(\theta^{Q_n}) = \frac{\theta(1-\xi) - z(1-\theta)K(\theta)}{(1-\xi)[\theta - zK(\theta)]} \tag{92}$$
for $0 < z < 1$, $0 < \theta < 1$.

(iii) *The p.g.f. of the limit distribution of Q_n is given by*
$$\frac{(1-\rho_1)(1-\theta)K(\theta)}{K(\theta) - \theta} \tag{93}$$
if $\rho_1 < 1$. Otherwise this p.g.f. is zero.

PROOF. (i) From the recurrence relations (72) we obtain $Q_n = S_n + 1 - m_{n-1}$, where $m_{n-1} = \min(0, S_1, S_2, \ldots, S_{n-1})$. Since each descending ladder step equals -1 with probability one, $-m_{n-1}$ is the number of descending ladder epochs up to τ_{n-1}, which is the number of idle periods up to τ_{n-1} minus the initial one (since we have assumed $Q_0 = 0$). Therefore $1 - m_{n-1} = \bar{N}(n)$, where $\bar{N}(n)$ is defined by (91).

(ii) Proceeding as in the proof of Theorem 5 we find that
$$P\{Q_n = 0\} = v_n,$$
$$P\{Q_n = j\} = \sum_{m=0}^{n-1} v_m u_{n-m}(j-1) \qquad (j \geq 1).$$

Using these and the results of Lemma 5 we arrive at the result (91) after some easy steps.

(iii) The relation $Q_n = S_n + 1 - m_{n-1}$ can also be written as $Q_n = X_n + S_{n-1} - m_{n-1}$. Lemma 1 now gives
$$Q_n \sim X_n + M_{n-1}.$$

This shows that $\lim Q_n$ exists in distribution. The p.g.f. of this limit is given by
$$\lim_{n\to\infty} E(\theta^{Q_n}) = \lim_{z\to 1}(1-z)\sum_0^\infty z^n E(\theta^{Q_n})$$
$$= \frac{(1-\rho_1)(1-\theta)K(\theta)}{K(\theta) - \theta} \quad \text{if } \rho_1 < 1,$$
$$= 0 \quad \text{if } \rho_1 \geq 1,$$
as desired. □

Theorem 20. *For the queue G/M/1 with $Q_0 = 0$ we have the following results.*

(i) *The queue length Q_n at $t_n - 0$ is given by*
$$Q_n = M_n - S_n. \tag{94}$$

(ii) *The distribution of Q_n has the transform given by*

$$(1 - z) \sum_{0}^{\infty} z^n E(\theta^{Q_n}) = \frac{1 - \zeta}{1 - \zeta\theta}. \tag{95}$$

(iii) *The limit distribution of Q_n is non-null if and only if $\rho_2 < 1$, in which case it is the geometric $(1 - \zeta)\zeta^j$ $(j \geq 0)$.*

PROOF. The result (i) follows easily from the recurrence relations (75). We have

$$P\{Q_n = j\} = \sum_{0}^{n} u_m v_{n-m}(j),$$

which leads to (ii). Finally

$$\lim_{z \to 1} (1 - z) \sum_{0}^{\infty} z^n E(\theta^{Q_n}) = \frac{1 - \zeta}{1 - \zeta\theta} \quad \text{if } \rho_2 < 1,$$
$$= 0 \text{ if } \rho_2 \geq 1,$$

and this yields the result (iii). □

Remark. For the two particular systems M/G/1 and G/M/1 we have obtained in sections 7 and 8 explicit expressions for various distributions or their transforms. In practice one might be merely interested in finding the means (and in some cases, variances) of the corresponding limit distributions. These are easily obtained from our results. Omitting the details of the calculations involved, we find that the mean waiting time $\bar{W}$ and mean queue length $\bar{Q}$ are given by

$$\bar{W} = \frac{\lambda E(v^2)}{2(1 - \rho_1)}, \qquad \bar{Q} = \rho_1 + \lambda \bar{W} \tag{96}$$

for the queue M/G/1, and

$$\bar{W} = \frac{\zeta}{\lambda(1 - \zeta)}, \qquad \bar{Q} = \lambda \bar{W} \tag{97}$$

for the queue G/M/1.

9 Further Remarks

(a) *Ladder Processes.* The concept of ladder points is due to Blackwell (1953), who used it in the proof of his renewal theorem. Feller (1959) used this concept and his theory of recurrent phenomena to simplify the fluctuation theory of sums of independent random variables. The pioneering work on fluctuation theory was done by Sparre Andersen (1953a, 1953b, 1954) using ingenious combinatorial methods. His work was extended by Spitzer (1956, 1960b). Mention must also be made of the results obtained by Baxter (1958) and Kemperman (1961) using analytical methods. Our treatment here follows Feller (1971).

(b) *Wiener–Hopf Factorization.* A comprehensive survey of Wiener–Hopf factorization and its use in solving integral equations of the type (98) is given by Krein (1958). Further references are given by Kemperman (1961). In the probability context great simplification is available owing to ladder processes.

(c) *Waiting Times.* Early work on the waiting times W_n was concerned with the limit distribution, and was based on Lindley's (1952) integral equation (98). The use of Wiener–Hopf techniques (in a nonprobabilistic context—see problem 9) in the solution of (98) was pointed out by Smith (1953), and in a probabilistic context by Spitzer (1957, 1960a). Spitzer also proved the existence of unbounded solutions of (98); see problems 6 7.

(d) *Heavy Traffic.* There exists a vast literature on limit theorems for queues with traffic intensity ≥ 1 (usually described as heavy traffic situation). Most of these use weak convergence of measures. Here we present only a few of the results for heavy traffic, our proofs being based on ladder processes. See also problems 11–12.

Problems

1. Prove the following relations:

   (i) $u_n(x) = \sum_{m=1}^{n} \int_{0+}^{x} f_m(dy) u_{n-m}(x-y), \ (n \geq 1, x > 0),$

   (ii) $v_n(x) = \sum_{m=1}^{n} \int_{x-}^{0+} g_m(dy) v_{n-m}(x-y), \ (n \geq 1, x \leq 0).$

2. Let $N(x)$ be the number of customers served during the busy period initiated by $W_0 = x > 0$ (excluding those present before the arrival at $n = 0$) and $I(x)$ the first idle period. Show that

   $$P\{N(x) = n, I(x) \geq -y\} = \sum_{m=0}^{n-1} \int_{-x+}^{0+} (-1)v_m(dz) g_{n-m}(y - x - z) \quad (n \geq 1, y \leq 0).$$

3. Continuation. For the queue M/G/1 show that

   $$Ez^{N(x)} = \xi e^{-(\lambda - \lambda\xi)x}.$$

4. Let $W_0 \geq 0$. Prove the following:

   (i) $W_n = W_0 + S_n + \mathscr{I}_n$ and $\mathscr{I}_n = -\min(0, W_0 + m_n).$

(ii) The limit distribution of W_n is independent of W_0.
(iii) The limit distribution of $\mathscr{I}_n$ is given by

$$\bar{F}_x(y) = (1 - \bar{p}) \sum_0^\infty v_n(-x - y) \quad \text{if } \alpha > 0,$$

$$= 0 \qquad \qquad \qquad \text{if } \alpha \leq 0,$$

where $W_0 = x \geq 0$.

5. The recurrence relations (1) show that $\{W_n, n \geq 0\}$ is a time-homogeneous Markov chain with the state space $[0, \infty)$. Let its transition d.f. be denoted by

$$F_n(x_0; x) = P\{W_n \leq x \mid W_0 = x_0\}.$$

(i) Prove that $F_1(x_0; x) = K(x - x_0)$.
(ii) As $n \to \infty$, prove that $F_n(x_0; x) \to F(x)$, where $F(x)$ is the unique solution of the integral equation

$$F(x) = \int_{0-}^\infty F(dy) K(x - y) \qquad (x \geq 0) \tag{98}$$

such that $F(x)$ is nondecreasing and right-continuous, $F(x) = 0$ for $x < 0$ and $F(x) \to 1$ as $x \to \infty$.

6. Continuation. For the queue G/M/1 with $E(X_k) = 0$, show that $F(x)$ defined by

$$F(x) = 0 \qquad \text{for } x < 0,$$

$$= 1 + \lambda x \quad \text{for } x \geq 0,$$

is a solution of (98), but obviously unbounded.

7. Busy Period Transitions. For $n \geq 1$, $x \geq 0$, let

$$^0F_n(x) = P\{W_1 > 0, W_2 > 0, \ldots, W_{n-1} > 0, W_n \leq x \mid W_0 = 0\}.$$

Prove that (i) $^0F(x) = \sum_1^\infty {^0F_n(x)} = u(x) + g(0) - 1$ and (ii) if $\alpha = 0$, then $^0F(x)$ is an unbounded solution of the integral equation (98).

8. Let $J_{n+1} = \min(0, X_{n+1} + W_n)$. Prove that if $\alpha \geq 0$, $J_{n+1} \to 0$ in distribution, while if $\alpha < 0$, the limit d.f. $G(x)$ of J_{n+1} is given by

$$G(x) = \int_{0-}^\infty dF(y) K(x - y) \qquad (x < 0).$$

(Assume that $K(x)$ is continuous.)

9. Wiener–Hopf Technique. In order to solve the equation (98) let us consider the auxiliary equation

$$G(x) = \int_{0-}^\infty dF(y) K(x - y) \qquad (x \leq 0). \tag{99}$$

It is clear that $G(x)$ is a monotone nondecreasing function with $G(-\infty) = 0$, $G(0) < \infty$. Let

$$F^*(\omega) = \int_{0-}^\infty e^{i\omega x} \, dF(x), \qquad G^*(\omega) = \int_{-\infty}^{0+} e^{i\omega x} \, dG(x), \tag{100}$$

be the Fourier transforms of F and G. Then from (98) and (99) it follows that

$$1 - \phi(\omega) = \frac{F(0) - G^*(\omega)}{F^*(\omega)}. \tag{101}$$

Using the Wiener–Hopf factorization (Theorem 1) prove that in the case $\alpha < 0$, the unique solution of (98)–(99) is given by

$$F^*(\omega) = F(0)[1 - E(e^{i\omega S_N})]^{-1}, \qquad G^*(\omega) = F(0)E(e^{i\omega S_{\bar N}}). \tag{102}$$

10. Continuation. In the queue M/G/1 prove that the function $G(x)$ defined by (99) is given by

$$G(x) = de^{\lambda x} \qquad (x \le 0)$$

where d is a constant. Use this result to prove the Pollaczek–Khintchine formula (70) for the Laplace transform of $F(x)$.

11. Let $E(u_n) = E(v_n) = a$ $(0 < a < \infty)$ and $\sigma^2 = \mathrm{Var}(v_n - u_n) < \infty$. If $B(x)$ is the busy period initiated by $W_0 = x \ge 0$ and $N(x)$ is as in problem 2, show that as $x \to \infty$

(i) $P\left\{\sigma^2 \cdot \dfrac{N(x)}{x^2} \le y\right\} \to G_{1/2}(y)$,

(ii) $P\left\{\dfrac{\sigma^2}{a} \cdot \dfrac{B(x)}{x^2} \le y\right\} \to G_{1/2}(y)$.

[Hint: $B(x) = x + v_1 + v_2 + \cdots + v_{N(x)}$; see Prabhu (1970).]

12. Continuation. Let $W_0 = 0$, B_k $(k \ge 1)$ the successive busy periods and $I(t)$ the total idle period up to time t. Prove that

(i) $P\left\{\dfrac{B_1 + B_2 + \cdots + B_k}{ac^2 k^2} \le x\right\} \to G_{1/2}(x)$, $(k \to \infty)$.

(ii) $P\left\{\dfrac{\sqrt{aI(t)}}{\sigma\sqrt{t}} \le x\right\} \to N_+(x)$, $(t \to \infty)$,

where c is the constant defined by (35).

13. Let C_n be the epoch of commencement of the nth customer's service, and $\mathscr{B}_n$ the duration of time up to t_n (the nth arrival epoch) that the server is busy. Show that the distribution of $(C_n, \mathscr{B}_n)$ in the given system is the same as in the dual system.

14. For the random walk of Lemma 5, let $\beta = K'(1)$ and $\gamma = K''(1) < \infty$. Prove the following:

(i) If $\beta > 1$, then $E(N) = (1 - \zeta)^{-1}$ and $E(S_N) = (\beta - 1)(1 - \zeta)^{-1}$.
(ii) If $\beta < 1$, then $E(\bar N) = (1 - \beta)^{-1}$.
(iii) If $\beta = 1$, then $E(N) = E(\bar N) = \infty$, $E(S_N) = \tfrac{1}{2}\gamma$.

15. For the queue M/G/1, let $Q_0 = i \ge 1$, and $T = \min\{n: Q_n = 0\}$. Show that $E(z^T) = \xi^i$ $(0 < z < 1)$.

16. For the queue G/M/1, let

$$^0P_{0j}^{(n)} = P\{Q_1 > 0, Q_2 > 0, \ldots, Q_{n-1} > 0, Q_n = j \mid Q_0 = 0\}$$

$(n \geq 1, j \geq 0)$. Show that if $\rho_2 < 1$,

$$\sum_{n=1}^{\infty} {}^0P_{0j}^{(n)} = \zeta^j \qquad (j \geq 0).$$

Chapter 2
Further Results for the Queue G/G/1

1 Transforms

In the preceding chapter we derived some basic results concerning ladder processes associated with a random walk, and applied them to the queueing systems M/M/1, G/M/1, and M/G/1. In these cases we were able to derive the various distributions by using the special properties of the random walk. We now proceed with the general discussion and derive the transforms of these distributions, establish the Wiener–Hopf factorization (stated earlier without proof) and derive further results for the single-server queue.

Let us recall that the random walk $\{S_n\}$ under consideration is induced by the d.f. $K(x)$. Let

$$K_n(x) = P\{S_n \leq x\} \qquad (n \geq 1, \ -\infty < x < \infty), \tag{1}$$

with $K_1(x) = K(x)$. The associated ladder processes are $\{N_k, S_{N_k}\}$ (ascending) and $\{\bar{N}_k, S_{\bar{N}_k}\}$ (descending), where as usual we denote $N_1 = N$, $\bar{N}_1 = \bar{N}$. Let

$$\chi(z, \omega) = E(z^N e^{i\omega S_N}), \qquad \bar{\chi}(z, \omega) = E(z^{\bar{N}} e^{i\omega S_{\bar{N}}}) \tag{2}$$

be the transforms of the distributions of the first ascending and first descending ladder points. For the renewal functions $u_n(x)$, $v_n(x)$ we introduce the transforms

$$u^*(z, \omega) = \sum_0^\infty z^n \int_{0-}^\infty e^{i\omega x} u_n(dx), \tag{3}$$

$$v^*(z, \omega) = \sum_0^\infty z^n (-1) \int_{-\infty}^{0+} e^{i\omega x} v_n(dx). \tag{4}$$

1 Transforms

All of the above transforms are defined for $0 < z < 1$ and ω real. The starting point of our discussion is the following combinatorial lemma due to Feller (1959), which we state without proof.[1]

Lemma 1. *For $n \geq 1$, $x > 0$ we have*

$$\sum_{1}^{\infty} \frac{1}{k} P\{N_k = n, S_n \leq x\} = \frac{1}{n} P\{0 < S_n \leq x\}. \tag{5}$$

Theorem 1. *For the transforms defined by* (2)–(4) *we have the following results*:

$$\chi(z, \omega) = 1 - \exp\left\{-\sum_{1}^{\infty} \frac{z^n}{n} \int_{0+}^{\infty} e^{i\omega x} K_n(dx)\right\}, \tag{6}$$

$$\bar{\chi}(z, \omega) = 1 - \exp\left\{-\sum_{1}^{\infty} \frac{z^n}{n} \int_{-\infty}^{0+} e^{i\omega x} K_n(dx)\right\}, \tag{7}$$

$$u^*(z, \omega) = \exp\left\{\sum_{1}^{\infty} \frac{z^n}{n} \int_{0+}^{\infty} e^{i\omega x} K_n(dx)\right\}, \tag{8}$$

$$v^*(z, \omega) = \exp\left\{\sum_{1}^{\infty} \frac{z^n}{n} \int_{-\infty}^{0+} e^{i\omega x} K_n(dx)\right\}. \tag{9}$$

PROOF. It suffices to prove (6) and (8), the proofs of (7) and (9) being similar. Using Lemma 1 we find that

$$\sum_{1}^{\infty} \frac{z^n}{n} \int_{0+}^{\infty} e^{i\omega x} K_n(dx) = \sum_{n=1}^{\infty} z^n \int_{0+}^{\infty} e^{i\omega x} \sum_{k=1}^{\infty} \frac{1}{k} P\{N_k = n, S_n \in dx\}$$

$$= \sum_{k=1}^{\infty} \frac{1}{k} E(z^{N_k} e^{i\omega S_{N_k}}) = \sum_{1}^{\infty} \frac{1}{k} [\chi(z, \omega)]^k$$

$$= \log[1 - \chi(z, \omega)]^{-1},$$

since the distribution of (N_k, S_{N_k}) is the k-fold convolution of the distribution of (N, S_N) with itself. This leads to (6). Also, since

$$u_n(x) = \sum_{k=0}^{\infty} P\{N_k = n, S_{N_k} \leq x\}$$

we obtain

$$u^*(z, \omega) = \sum_{k=0}^{\infty} E(z^{N_k} e^{i\omega S_{N_k}}) = \sum_{0}^{\infty} [\chi(z, \omega)]^k = [1 - \chi(z, \omega)]^{-1},$$

which gives (8). The proof is thus complete. □

We noted that for fixed z in $(0, 1)$ the transforms $\chi(z, \omega)$ and $\bar{\chi}(z, \omega)$ are bounded analytic functions for $I_m(\omega) \geq 0$ and $I_m(\omega) \leq 0$ respectively.

---
[1] See Feller (1971), p. 412.

Theorem 1 shows that $1 - \chi$ and $1 - \bar{\chi}$ are bounded away from zero. Furthermore, letting $\omega = \omega_1 + i\omega_2$ (ω_1, ω_2 real) we find that

$$|\chi(z, \omega)| \leq E(z^N |e^{i\omega S_N}|) < E(e^{-\omega_2 S_N}) \to 0$$

as $\omega_2 \to \infty$. Theorem 2 below shows that $1 - \chi$ and $1 - \bar{\chi}$ provide a unique factorization of $1 - z\phi(\omega)$ for ω real.

Theorem 2. *Let $\phi(\omega) = E(e^{i\omega X_1})$. (i) Then*

$$1 - z\phi(\omega) = [1 - \chi(z, \omega)][1 - \bar{\chi}(z, \omega)] \qquad (0 < z < 1, \omega \text{ real}). \qquad (10)$$

(ii) Let $D(z, \omega)$ and $\bar{D}(z, \omega)$ be functions such that for fixed z in $(0, 1)$, they are bounded analytic functions for $\mathrm{Im}(\omega) \geq 0$ and $\mathrm{Im}(\omega) \leq 0$ respectively, bounded away from zero, $D(z, w) \to 1$ as $\mathrm{Im}(\omega) \to \infty$, and

$$1 - z\phi(\omega) = D(z, \omega)\bar{D}(z, \omega) \qquad (0 < z < 1, \omega \text{ real}). \qquad (11)$$

Then $D(z, \omega) = 1 - \chi(z, \omega)$ and $\bar{D}(z, \omega) = 1 - \bar{\chi}(z, \omega)$.

PROOF. (i) Using the results (6)–(7) we find that

$$[1 - \chi(z, \omega)][1 - \bar{\chi}(z, \omega)] = \exp\left\{-\sum_1^\infty \frac{z^n}{n} \int_{-\infty}^\infty e^{i\omega x} K_n(dx)\right\}$$

$$= \exp\left\{-\sum_1^\infty \frac{z^n}{n} \phi(\omega)^n\right\}$$

$$= 1 - z\phi(\omega).$$

(ii) We have $(1 - \chi)(1 - \bar{\chi}) = D(z, \omega)\bar{D}(z, \omega)$ for ω real, and

$$\Phi(\omega) = \frac{1 - \chi}{D} \quad \text{for } \mathrm{Im}(\omega) \geq 0$$

$$= \frac{\bar{D}}{1 - \bar{\chi}} \quad \text{for } \mathrm{Im}(\omega) \leq 0$$

defines a bounded entire function such that $\Phi(\omega) \to 1$ as $\mathrm{Im}(\omega) \to \infty$. By Liouville's theorem $\Phi(\omega) \equiv 1$ and therefore $1 - \chi \equiv D$, $1 - \bar{\chi} \equiv \bar{D}$, as required. The proof is thus complete (see also Problem 1). □

Let us now define

$$A = \sum_1^\infty \frac{1}{n} P\{S_n \leq 0\}, \qquad B = \sum_1^\infty \frac{1}{n} P\{S_n > 0\}. \qquad (12)$$

We have $A + B = \sum n^{-1} = \infty$, so at least one of the above series must diverge (see Problems 2–3). The following is a restatement of Theorem 2 of Chapter 1, but it should be noted that the proof given there does not use the explicit results for the transforms (6)–(7).

1 Transforms

Theorem 3. (i) *If* $A = B = \infty$, *then* N *and* $\bar{N}$ *are both proper and have infinite means.*

(ii) *If* $A < \infty$, *then* N *is proper, with* $E(N) = e^A < \infty$ *while* $\bar{N}$ *is defective.*

(iii) *If* $B < \infty$, *then* $\bar{N}$ *is proper, with* $E(\bar{N}) = e^B < \infty$, *while* N *is defective.*

PROOF. Letting $\omega = 0$ in (6)–(7) we obtain

$$E(z^N) = 1 - \exp\left[-\sum_1^\infty \frac{z^n}{n} P\{S_n > 0\}\right], \tag{13}$$

$$E(z^{\bar{N}}) = 1 - \exp\left[-\sum_1^\infty \frac{z^n}{n} P\{S_n \leq 0\}\right]. \tag{14}$$

These give

$$p = P\{N < \infty\} = 1 - e^{-B}, \qquad \bar{p} = P\{\bar{N} < \infty\} = 1 - e^{-A}.$$

If $B = \infty$, then N is proper and

$$E(N) = \lim_{z \to 1} \frac{1 - E(z^N)}{1 - z} = \lim_{z \to 1} \exp\left[\sum_1^\infty \frac{z^n}{n} P\{S_n \leq 0\}\right]$$

$$= e^A \leq \infty.$$

Similarly, if $A = \infty$, then $E(\bar{N}) = e^B \leq \infty$. These results lead to the statements of the theorem. □

It remains to derive the transform of the distribution of $(M_n, M_n - S_n)$, which was obtained in the preceding chapter. By Theorem 5 of that chapter we have

$$P\{M_n \leq x, M_n - S_n \leq y\} = P\{S_n - m_n \leq x, m_n \geq -y\}$$
$$= \sum_0^n u_m(x) v_{n-m}(-y) \quad (n \geq 0, x \geq 0, y \geq 0). \tag{15}$$

It is convenient to introduce the measure $v_z(dx)$, where

$$v_z(dx) = \sum_1^\infty \frac{z^n}{n} K_n(dx) \quad (x \neq 0), \; v_z\{0\} = 0. \tag{16}$$

For fixed z in $(0, 1)$, v_z is a Lévy measure—that is,

$$\int_0^\infty \min(1, x^2) v_z(dx) < \infty. \tag{17}$$

In fact, v_z is a finite measure, since

$$\int_{-\infty}^\infty v_z(dx) = \sum_1^\infty \frac{z^n}{n} P\{S_n > 0\} \leq \sum_1^\infty \frac{z^n}{n} < \infty.$$

Theorem 4 below exhibits the required transform as a product of compound Poisson characteristic functions with Lévy measure v_z restricted to $(0, \infty)$ and $(-\infty, 0)$ respectively. It turns out that the limit distributions of M_n and m_n are compound Poisson (Theorem 5).

Theorem 4. *For $0 < z < 1$, ω real we have*

$$(1-z)\sum_0^\infty z^n E[e^{i\omega_1 M_n + i\omega_2(M_n - S_n)}]$$

$$= (1-z)\sum_0^\infty z^n E[e^{i\omega_1(S_n - m_n) - i\omega_2 m_n}] \tag{18}$$

$$= \exp\left\{\int_0^\infty (e^{i\omega_1 x} - 1)v_z(dx) + \int_{-\infty}^0 (e^{-i\omega_2 x} - 1)v_z(dx)\right\}.$$

PROOF. From (15) we obtain

$$\sum_0^\infty z^n E[e^{i\omega_1 M_n + i\omega_2(M_n - S_n)}] = \sum_{m=0}^\infty z^m \int_0^\infty e^{i\omega_1 x} u_m(dx) \sum_{n=m}^\infty z^{n-m} \int_{-\infty}^0 e^{-i\omega_2 y} v_{n-m}(dy)$$

$$= u^*(z, \omega_1) v^*(z, -\omega_2).$$

The required results now follow from (8)–(9), and the result

$$1 - z = \exp\left[-\sum_1^\infty \frac{z^n}{n} P\{S_n > 0\} - \sum_1^\infty \frac{z^n}{n} P\{S_n \leq 0\}\right]. \qquad \square$$

Theorem 5. (i) $B < \infty$, *the limit d.f. on M_n has the c.f.*

$$\exp\left[\int_0^\infty (e^{i\omega x} - 1)v_1(dx)\right]. \tag{19}$$

(ii) *If $A < \infty$, then the limit d.f. of m_n has the c.f.*

$$\exp\left[\int_{-\infty}^0 (e^{i\omega x} - 1)v_1(dx)\right]. \tag{20}$$

PROOF. From (18) we obtain

$$(1-z)\sum_0^\infty z^n E(e^{i\omega M_n}) = e^{\int_0^\infty (e^{i\omega x} - 1)v_z(dx)}.$$

We have seen that $M_n \to M < \infty$ with probability one iff $p < 1$ ($B < \infty$). The c.f. of M is then given by

$$\lim_{z \to 1}(1-z)\sum_0^\infty z^n E(e^{i\omega M_n}) = \exp\left\{\int_0^\infty (e^{i\omega x} - 1)v_1(dx)\right\}.$$

We have thus proved (19). The proof of (20) is similar. $\square$

2 Further Applications to the Queue G/G/1

In the study of the random walk underlying a single-server queue we have not so far used the fact that $X_n = v_n - u_n$, where v_n and u_n are independent non-negative random variables. This fact somewhat restricts the class of distributions of X_n that we may consider in queueing problems. Thus by a theorem of H. Cramér, X_n cannot in particular have a normal distribution. On the other hand one would expect this special structure of X_n to yield additional results of importance to queueing theory. It turns out that such is indeed the case.

Let us denote by $A(x)$ and $B(x)$ the d.f.'s of inter-arrival times u_n and service times v_n respectively, and by $\phi_1(\omega)$ and $\phi_2(\omega)$ their c.f.'s. The c.f. of X_n is then given by

$$\phi(\omega) = \phi_1(-\omega)\phi_2(\omega). \tag{21}$$

Also, for $n \geq 1$, let $U_n = u_1 + u_2 + \cdots + u_n$, $V_n = v_1 + v_2 + \cdots + v_n$, and

$$A_n(x) = P\{U_n \leq x\}, \qquad B_n(x) = P\{V_n \leq x\} \tag{22}$$

with $A_1(x) = A(x)$ and $B_1(x) = B(x)$.

We have already seen that the number of customers served during the first busy period is given by $\bar{N}$, the first descending ladder epoch of the underlying random walk. The busy period and the idle period that follows it are given respectively by

$$V = v_1 + v_2 + \cdots + v_{\bar{N}}, \qquad I = -S_{\bar{N}}, \tag{23}$$

and the busy cycle by

$$U = V + I = u_1 + u_2 + \cdots + u_{\bar{N}}. \tag{24}$$

We first note from Theorem 3 that the random variable $\bar{N}$ is proper if and only if $A = \infty$, in which case (and only then) the random variables U and V are also proper. Furthermore $E(\bar{N}) = e^B \leq \infty$, and

$$E(I) = (-\alpha)e^B < \infty \quad \text{if } \alpha < 0. \tag{25}$$

From (23) and (24) we also find that

$$E(U) = aE(\bar{N}), \qquad E(V) = bE(\bar{N}) \tag{26}$$

where a and b are the mean inter-arrival and service times respectively.[2] Other variables of interest are

$$C_n = U_n + W_n, \qquad D_{n+1} = U_n + W_n + v_{n+1}, \qquad \mathscr{B}_n = U_n - \mathscr{I}_n, \tag{27}$$

where C_n is the epoch of commencement of the nth customer's service, D_{n+1} the epoch of his departure from the system and $\mathscr{B}_n$ the duration of

---

[2] The result (25) is the so-called Wald equation of sequential analysis, and (26) can be established in the same manner.

time up to t_n that the server is busy. Information concerning these can be obtained by a slight modification of the results of section 1, as is shown by the following.

Theorem 6. *For $0 < z < 1$, $\theta_1 \geq 0$, $\theta_2 \geq 0$, ω real we have*

$$E(z^N e^{-\theta_1 U_N - \theta_2 V_N + i\omega S_N})$$
$$= 1 - \exp\left\{-\sum_1^\infty \frac{z^n}{n} \int_0^\infty \int_0^\infty e^{i\omega x - \theta_1 u - \theta_2(u+x)} A_n(du) B_n(u+dx)\right\} \tag{28}$$

and

$$E(z^{\bar{N}} e^{-\theta_1 U_{\bar{N}} - \theta_2 V_{\bar{N}} + i\omega S_{\bar{N}}})$$
$$= 1 - \exp\left\{-\sum_1^\infty \frac{z^n}{n} \int_{-\infty}^{0-} \int_0^\infty e^{i\omega x - \theta_1 u - \theta_2(u+x)} A_n(du) B_n(u+dx)\right\}. \tag{29}$$

PROOF. For $\theta_1 = \theta_2 = 0$ the above results reduce to those already proved. We shall therefore assume that $\theta_1 > 0$, $\theta_2 > 0$ and put $\theta = (\theta_1, \theta_2)$. In the description of the given single-server queue let us replace the d.f.'s $A(x)$ and $B(x)$ by $A_{\theta_1}(x)$ and $B_{\theta_2}(x)$, where

$$A_{\theta_1}(dx) = e^{-\theta_1 x} A(dx), \qquad B_{\theta_2}(dx) = e^{-\theta_2 x} B(dx). \tag{30}$$

The n-fold convolution of $A_{\theta_1}(x)$ with itself is given by $A_{n\theta_1}(dx) = e^{-\theta_1 x} A_n(dx)$, and the n-fold convolution of $B_{\theta_2}(x)$ with itself is given by $B_{n\theta_2}(dx) = e^{-\theta_2 x} B_n(dx)$ $(n \geq 1)$. For this modified random walk $\{S_{n\theta}, n \geq 1\}$ let $K_{n\theta}(x)$ be the d.f. of $S_{n\theta}$. We have

$$K_{n\theta}(dx) = \int_{u=0}^\infty e^{-\theta_1 u - \theta_2(u+x)} A_n(du) B_n(u+dx). \tag{31}$$

For the first ascending ladder epoch N_θ of this random walk we have

$$P\{N_\theta = n, S_{N_\theta} \in dx\} = \int A_{\theta_1}(du_1) A_{\theta_1}(du_2) \cdots A_{\theta_1}(du_n) B_{\theta_2}(dv_1) \cdots B_{\theta_2}(dv_n)$$

$$= \int e^{-\theta_1 U_n - \theta_2 V_n} A(du_1) A(du_2) \cdots A(du_n) B(dv_1) \cdots B(dv_n),$$

where the integral is taken over the region $V_1 - U_1 \leq 0$, $V_2 - U_2 \leq 0$, ..., $V_{n-1} - U_{n-1} \leq 0$, $V_n - U_n \in dx$. It follows that

$$P\{N_\theta = n, S_{N_\theta} \in dx\} = E(e^{-\theta_1 U_n - \theta_2 V_n}; N = n, S_n \in dx), \tag{32}$$

and therefore

$$E(z^N e^{-\theta_1 U_N - \theta_2 V_N + i\omega S_N}) = E(z^{N_\theta} e^{i\omega S_{N_\theta}})$$

$$= 1 - \exp\left\{-\sum_1^\infty \frac{z^n}{n} \int_{0+}^\infty e^{i\omega x} K_{n\theta}(dx)\right\};$$

and this last expression simplifies to the right side of (28). We have thus proved (28). The proof of (29) is similar. □

Theorem 7. For $0 < z < 1$, $\theta_1 \geq 0$, $\theta_2 \geq 0$, ω real we have

$$1 - z\phi_1(-\omega + i\theta_1)\phi_2(\omega + i\theta_2) = [1 - \chi_\theta(z, \omega)][1 - \bar{\chi}_\theta(z, \omega)], \quad (33)$$

where $\chi_\theta(z, \omega)$ and $\bar{\chi}_\theta(z, \omega)$ are the transforms on the left sides of (28) and (29) respectively. Furthermore the factorization (33) is unique in the same sense as (10).

PROOF. The required result is the Wiener–Hopf factorization for the modified random walk $\{S_{n\theta}\}$, since

$$\phi_\theta(\omega) = E(e^{i\omega S_{1\theta}}) = \int_0^\infty e^{i\omega v} B_{\theta_2}(dv) \int_0^\infty e^{-i\omega u} A_{\theta_1}(du) \quad (34)$$

$$= \phi_2(\omega + i\theta_2)\phi_1(-\omega + i\theta_1). \quad \square$$

Theorem 8. For $0 < z < 1$, $\theta_1 \geq 0$, $\theta_2 \geq 0$, ω_1, ω_2 real we have

$$[1 - z\psi_1(\theta_1)\psi_2(\theta_2)] \sum_0^\infty z^n E[e^{-\theta_1 U_n - \theta_2 V_n + i\omega_1 W_n + i\omega_2 \mathscr{I}_n}]$$

$$= \exp\left\{\int_0^\infty (e^{i\omega_1 x} - 1)v_{z\theta}(dx) + \int_{-\infty}^0 (e^{-i\omega_2 x} - 1)v_{z\theta}(dx)\right\}, \quad (35)$$

where ψ_1, ψ_2 are the Laplace transforms of the d.f.'s A, B respectively, and the measure $v_{z\theta}$ is defined by

$$v_{z\theta}(dx) = \sum_1^\infty \frac{1}{n} K_{n\theta}(dx) \quad (x \neq 0), \quad v_{z\theta}\{0\} = 0. \quad (36)$$

PROOF. Since $W_n = S_n - m_n$, $\mathscr{I}_n = -m_n$ we have

$$\sum_0^\infty z^n E[e^{-\theta_1 U_n - \theta_2 V_n + i\omega_1 W_n + i\omega_2 \mathscr{I}_n}] = \sum_0^\infty z^n E[e^{-\theta_1 U_n - \theta_2 V_n + i\omega_1(S_n - m_n) + i\omega_2(-m_n)}]$$

$$= \sum_0^\infty z^n E[e^{i\omega_1(S_{n\theta} - m_{n\theta}) - i\omega_2 m_{n\theta}}],$$

where $m_{n\theta} = \min(0, S_{1\theta}, S_{2\theta}, \ldots, S_{n\theta})$. By Theorem 4 this last sum

$$= [1 - \chi_\theta(z, \omega_1)]^{-1}[1 - \bar{\chi}_\theta(z, -\omega_2)]^{-1}. \quad (37)$$

Also, putting $\omega_1 = \omega_2 = 0$ in (33) we obtain

$$1 - z\psi_1(\theta_1)\psi_2(\theta_2) = [1 - \chi_\theta(z, 0)][1 - \bar{\chi}_\theta(z, 0)]. \quad (38)$$

From (37) and (38) we obtain the desired result. □

Theorem 8 is a comprehensive result concerning the single-server queue. Putting $\theta_2 = 0$, $\omega_2 = 0$ in (35) we obtain the transform of the joint distribution of the nth customer's arrival epoch U_n and his waiting time W_n. The transform of the distribution of $\mathscr{B}_n$ and C_n [see equation (27)] can also be obtained from (35) as follows.

Theorem 9. *For $0 < z < 1$, $\theta_1 \geq \theta_2 \geq 0$ we have*

$$[1 - z\psi_1(\theta_1)\psi_2(\theta_2)] \sum_0^\infty z^n E[e^{-\theta_1 C_n - \theta_2 \mathscr{B}_n}]$$

$$= \exp\left\{\sum_1^\infty \frac{z^n}{n} \iint_{v-u>0} (e^{-\theta_1 v - \theta_2 u} - e^{-\theta_2 v - \theta_1 u}) A_n(du) B_n(dv)\right\}. \tag{39}$$

PROOF. Since $C_n = U_n + W_n$ and $\mathscr{B}_n = U_n - \mathscr{I}_n = V_n - W_n$ we have

$$\sum_0^\infty z^n E[e^{-\theta_1 C_n - \theta_2 \mathscr{B}_n}] = \sum_0^\infty z^n E[e^{-\theta_1 U_n - \theta_2 V_n - (\theta_1 - \theta_2) W_n}].$$

Using (35) we find that this last sum

$$= [1 - z\psi_1(\theta_1)\psi_2(\theta_2)]^{-1} \exp\left\{\int_0^\infty (e^{-(\theta_1 - \theta_2)x} - 1) v_{z\theta}(dx)\right\}$$

$$= [1 - z\psi_1(\theta_1)\psi_2(\theta_2)]^{-1}$$

$$\times \exp\left\{\sum_1^\infty \frac{z^n}{n} \int_0^\infty \int_0^\infty (e^{-(\theta_1 - \theta_2)x} - 1) e^{-\theta_1 u - \theta_2(u+x)} A_n(du) B_n(u+dx)\right\}$$

which leads to the desired result. □

For easy reference we state below the result concerning the number $\bar{N}$ of customers served during a busy period, the duration $V = V_{\bar{N}}$ of this busy period and the duration $I = -S_{\bar{N}}$ of the idle period that follows.

Theorem 10. *For $0 < z < 1$, $\theta_1 \geq 0$, $\theta_2 \geq 0$ we have*

$$E(z^{\bar{N}} e^{-\theta_1 V - \theta_2 I}) = 1 - \exp\left\{-\sum_1^\infty \frac{z^n}{n} \iint_{v-u \leq 0} e^{-\theta_1 v + \theta_2(v-u)} A_n(du) B_n(dv)\right\}. \tag{40}$$

PROOF. The required transform is $\bar{\chi}_\theta(z, -i\theta_2)$ with $\theta = (0, \theta_1)$ and the result follows from (29). □

3 The Queues G/M/1 and M/G/1

The special cases G/M/1 and M/G/1 were considered in section 7 of the preceding chapter where we derived results concerning the waiting time, idle time and the number of customers served during a busy period. We shall now also consider the duration of the busy period in these systems. Our technique consists of modifying the given distributions of inter-arrival times and service times as in (30).

3.1 The Queue G/M/1

Let the inter-arrival distribution be $e^{-\theta_1 u}H(du)$ and the service time density $\lambda e^{-(\theta_2 + \lambda)x}$, where $\theta_1 \geq 0$, $\theta_2 \geq 0$. Denote $\theta = (\theta_1, \theta_2)$. The d.f. of $X_n = v_n - u_n$ is then given by

$$K_{1\theta}(x) = \int_{-x}^{\infty} \frac{\lambda}{\theta_2 + \lambda} e^{-\theta_1 u}[1 - e^{-(\theta_2 + \lambda)(u+x)}]H(du) \quad \text{for } x \leq 0 \quad (41)$$

$$= c_1 - c_2 e^{-(\theta_2 + \lambda)x} \quad \text{for } x \geq 0,$$

where

$$c_1 = \frac{\lambda \psi(\theta_1)}{\theta_2 + \lambda}, \quad c_2 = \frac{\lambda \psi(\theta_1 + \theta_2 + \lambda)}{\theta_2 + \lambda}. \quad (42)$$

This d.f. has the partial lack of memory property

$$P\{X_k - x \leq y | x < X_k < \infty\} = 1 - e^{-(\theta_2 + \lambda)y} \quad (43)$$

for $y > x \geq 0$. Proceeding as in section 7 of the preceding chapter we find that

$$\chi_\theta(z, \omega) = E[z^{N_\theta} \exp(i\omega S_{N_\theta})] = \frac{\lambda \Gamma}{\theta_2 + \lambda - i\omega}, \quad (44)$$

$$\bar{\chi}_\theta(z, \omega) = E[z^{\bar{N}_\theta} \exp(i\omega S_{\bar{N}_\theta})] = \lambda \frac{z\phi_1(-\omega + i\theta_1) - \Gamma}{\theta_2 + \lambda - \lambda\Gamma - i\omega}, \quad (45)$$

where $\Gamma \equiv \Gamma(z, \theta_1 + \theta_2)$ is the unique continuous solution of the equation

$$\Gamma = z\psi(\theta_1 + \theta_2 + \lambda - \lambda\Gamma), \quad (46)$$

with $\Gamma(z, \infty) = 0$. These results lead to the following.

Theorem 11. *In the queue G/M/1 the joint distribution of $\bar{N}$, the number of customers served during a busy period, the duration $V = V_{\bar{N}}$ of this busy period and the duration $I = -S_{\bar{N}}$ of the idle period that follows it has the transform*

$$E(z^{\bar{N}} e^{-\theta_1 V - \theta_2 I}) = \lambda \frac{z\psi(\theta_2) - \Gamma}{\theta_1 - \theta_2 + \lambda - \lambda\Gamma}, \quad (47)$$

where $\Gamma \equiv \Gamma(z, \theta_1)$ is the unique continuous solution of the equation $\Gamma = z\psi(\theta_1 + \lambda - \lambda\Gamma)$ with $\Gamma(z, \infty) = 0$.

PROOF. The required transform is given by
$$\tilde{\chi}_\theta(z, \omega) = E(z^{\bar{N}} e^{-\theta_1 U_{\bar{N}} - \theta_2 V_{\bar{N}} + i\omega S_{\bar{N}}})$$
with $(\theta_1, \theta_2, i\omega)$ replaced by $(0, \theta_1, \theta_2)$. □

3.2 The Queue M/G/1

This system is the dual of the queue G/M/1 considered above. Using primes to denote the random variables of the system we have
$$(N', V'_{\bar{N}'}, S'_{\bar{N}'}) \sim (N, U_N, -S_N), \tag{48}$$
so that
$$E(z^{\bar{N}'} e^{-\theta_1 V' - \theta_2 I'}) = E(z^N e^{-\theta_1 U_N - \theta_2 S_N}); \tag{49}$$
and this latter transform is given by $\chi_\theta(z, \omega)$ with $(\theta_1, \theta_2, i\omega)$ replaced by $(\theta_1, 0, -\theta_2)$. We thus obtain the following result.

Theorem 12. *In the queue M/G/1 we have*
$$E(z^{\bar{N}'} e^{-\theta_1 V' - \theta_2 I'}) = \frac{\lambda \Gamma}{\theta_2 + \lambda}, \tag{50}$$
where Γ is as in Theorem 11.

Theorem 13. *In the queue M/M/1 we have*
$$E(z^{\bar{N}'} e^{-\theta V'}) = \Gamma, \tag{51}$$
where $\Gamma \equiv \Gamma(z, \theta)$ is given by
$$\Gamma = \frac{\theta + \lambda + \mu - \sqrt{(\theta + \lambda + \mu)^2 - 4\lambda\mu z}}{2\lambda}. \tag{52}$$

PROOF. In this case we have $\psi(\theta) = \mu(\mu + \theta)^{-1}$, and the equation for Γ reduces to
$$\lambda \Gamma^2 - (\theta + \lambda + \mu)\Gamma + \mu z = 0.$$
The solution of this with $\Gamma(z, \infty) = 0$ is given by (52). □

4 The Queue G/E_k/1

In this system the inter-arrival times u_n have the d.f. $H(x)$ and the service times v_n have the gamma density
$$e^{-\lambda x} \lambda^k \frac{x^{k-1}}{(k-1)!} \quad (x > 0), \tag{53}$$

4 The Queue G/E$_k$/1

where $0 < \lambda < \infty$ and k is a positive integer. The c.f. of $X_n = v_n - u_n$ is given by

$$E(e^{i\omega X_n}) = \left(\frac{\lambda}{\lambda - i\omega}\right)^k \phi_1(-\omega), \tag{54}$$

where $\phi_1(\omega)$ is the c.f. of $H(x)$. For $k = 1$ this reduces to the case considered in section 3, where the partial lack of memory property of the distribution was used to derive various results. For $k > 1$ we rely on the Wiener–Hopf factorization (33). We shall also need the Laplace transform

$$\psi(\theta) = \int_0^\infty e^{-\theta x} H(dx) \qquad (\theta > 0). \tag{55}$$

Obviously $\psi(\theta) = \phi_1(i\theta)$. We assume that $0 < -\psi'(0) < \infty$. The traffic intensity of the system is given by $\rho_2 = -k[\lambda\psi'(0)]^{-1} < \infty$. Finally, $\alpha = E(X_n) = k(\lambda\rho_2)^{-1}(\rho_2 - 1)$.

Lemma 2. *For the random walk induced by the c.f.* (54) *we have*

$$\chi_\theta(z, \omega) = 1 - \prod_{r=1}^k \left(1 - \frac{\lambda\gamma_r}{\theta_2 + \lambda - i\omega}\right), \tag{56}$$

$$\bar{\chi}_\theta(z, \omega) = 1 - \frac{(\theta_2 + \lambda - i\omega)^k - z\lambda^k \phi_1(-\omega + i\theta_1)}{\prod_{r=1}^k (\theta_2 + \lambda - \lambda\gamma_r - i\omega)}, \tag{57}$$

where $0 < z < 1$, $\theta_1 \geq 0$, $\theta_2 \geq 0$, ω *real and* $\gamma_r \equiv \gamma_r(z, \theta_1 + \theta_2)$ *are the roots of the equation*

$$\gamma^k = z\psi(\theta_1 + \theta_2 + \lambda - \lambda\gamma), \tag{58}$$

with $|\gamma_r| < 1$ $(r = 1, 2, \ldots, k)$.

PROOF. The Wiener–Hopf factorization (33) in this case is given by

$$\frac{(\theta_2 + \lambda - i\omega)^k - z\lambda^k \phi_1(-\omega + i\theta_1)}{(\theta_2 + \lambda - i\omega)^k} = [1 - \chi_\theta(z, \omega)][1 - \bar{\chi}_\theta(z, \omega)]. \tag{59}$$

Now consider the equation $(\theta_2 + \lambda - i\omega)^k - z\lambda^k \phi_1(-\omega + i\theta_1) = 0$. The transformation $\lambda\gamma = \theta_2 + \lambda - i\omega$ reduces this to the equation (58), and Theorem A2 shows that the latter equation has exactly k roots with $|\gamma_r| < 1$. Let us write the left side of (59) as $D \cdot \bar{D}$, where

$$D = \prod_{r=1}^k \left(\frac{\theta_2 + \lambda - \lambda\gamma - i\omega}{\theta_2 + \lambda - i\omega}\right),$$

$$\bar{D} = \frac{(\theta_2 + \lambda - i\omega)^k - z\lambda^k \phi_1(-\omega + i\theta_1)}{\prod_{r=1}^k (\theta_2 + \lambda - \lambda\gamma - i\omega)}.$$

For fixed $0 < z < 1$, $\theta_1 \geq 0$, $\theta_2 \geq 0$, the factors D, $\bar{D}$ are bounded analytic functions, which are bounded away from zero in the half-planes Im$(\omega) \geq 0$,

Im$(\omega) \leq 0$ respectively. Also, $D \to 1$ as Im$(\omega) \to \infty$. By uniqueness of the factorization it follows that $D = 1 - \chi_\theta$ and $\bar{D} = 1 - \bar{\chi}_\theta$ and the theorem is proved. □

Theorem 14. *For the queue* G/E_k/1 *we have*

$$E(z^{\bar{N}}e^{-\theta_1 V - \theta_2 I}) = 1 - \frac{(\theta_1 - \theta_2 + \lambda)^k - z\lambda^k \psi(\theta_2)}{\prod_{r=1}^k (\theta_1 - \theta_2 + \lambda - \lambda\gamma_r)}, \quad (60)$$

where $0 < z < 1$, $\theta_1 \geq 0$, $\theta_2 \geq 0$ *and* $\gamma_r = \gamma_r(z, \theta_1)$ $(r = 1, 2, \ldots, k)$.

PROOF. We use the result (57) with $(\theta_1, \theta_2, i\omega)$ replaced by $(0, \theta_1, \theta_2)$. □

Putting $\theta_1 = 0$, $\theta_2 = 0$ in (56)–(57) we obtain

$$\chi_0(z, \omega) = 1 - \prod_{r=1}^k \left(1 - \frac{\lambda\xi_r}{\lambda - i\omega}\right), \quad (61)$$

$$\bar{\chi}_0(z, \omega) = 1 - \frac{(\lambda - i\omega)^k - z\lambda^k \phi_1(-\omega)}{\prod_{r=1}^k (\lambda - \lambda\xi_r - i\omega)}, \quad (62)$$

where $\xi_r \equiv \xi_r(z)$ are the roots of the equation

$$\xi^k = z\psi(\lambda - \lambda\xi), \quad (63)$$

with $|\xi_r| < 1$ $(r = 1, 2, \ldots, k)$. As $z \to 1$, $\xi_r(z) \to \zeta_r$, where ζ_r $(r = 1, 2, \ldots, k)$ are the roots of the equation

$$\zeta^k = \psi(\lambda - \lambda\zeta). \quad (64)$$

From Theorem A2 we see that if $\rho_2 < 1$, then $|\zeta_r| < 1$ $(r = 1, 2, \ldots, k)$, whereas if $\rho_2 \geq 1$, then $|\zeta_r| < 1$ $(r = 1, 2, \ldots, k-1)$ and $\zeta_k = 1$.

Theorem 15. *For the queue* G/E_k/1 *we have*:
(i)

$$\sum_0^\infty z^n E(e^{i\omega_1 W_n + i\omega_2 \mathscr{I}_n}) = \frac{(\lambda - i\omega_1)^k}{(\lambda + i\omega_2)^k - z\lambda^k \phi_1(\omega_2)} \prod_{r=1}^k \left(\frac{\lambda - \lambda\xi_r + i\omega_2}{\lambda - \lambda\xi_r - i\omega_1}\right). \quad (65)$$

(ii)

$$\lim_{n \to \infty} E(e^{i\omega W_n}) = (\lambda - i\omega)^k \prod_{r=1}^k \left(\frac{1 - \zeta_r}{\lambda - \lambda\zeta_r - i\omega}\right) \quad (\rho_2 < 1).$$

(iii)

$$\lim_{n \to \infty} E(e^{i\omega \mathscr{I}_n}) = \frac{k(1 - \rho_2^{-1})i\omega}{(\lambda + i\omega)^k - \lambda^k \phi_1(\omega)} \prod_{r=1}^{k-1} \left(\frac{\lambda - \lambda\zeta_r + i\omega}{1 - \zeta_r}\right) \quad (\rho_2 > 1).$$

PROOF. The result (i) follows from Theorem 4. To prove (ii) we note that

$$(1-z)\sum_{0}^{\infty} z^n E(e^{i\omega W_n}) = (\lambda - i\omega)^k \prod_{r=1}^{k} \left(\frac{1-\xi_r}{\lambda - \lambda\xi_r - i\omega}\right).$$

Letting $z \to 1$ in this we obtain (ii). Finally we have

$$(1-z)\sum_{0}^{\infty} z^n E(e^{i\omega \mathscr{I}_n}) = \frac{1-z}{(\lambda + i\omega)^k - z\lambda^k\phi_1(\omega)} \prod_{r=1}^{k} \left(\frac{\lambda - \lambda\xi_r + i\omega}{1-\xi_r}\right).$$

Letting $z \to 1$ in this we obtain (iii), since

$$\lim_{z\to 1} \frac{1-z}{1-\xi_k} = \xi'_k(1)^{-1} = k(1-\rho_2^{-1}). \qquad \square$$

5 The Queue $E_k/G/1$

The queue $E_k/G/1$ is the dual of $G/E_k/1$, that is, here the inter-arrival times have the density (53) and the service times have the d.f. $H(x)$ with the Laplace transform $\psi(\theta)$. The traffic intensity is $\rho_1 = -\lambda\psi'(0)/k < \infty$. It is useful to note that $\rho_1\rho_2 = 1$. The results for this queue follow from Theorems 12 and 13 of the preceding chapter.[3]

Theorem 16. *For the queue $E_k/G/1$ we have*

$$E(z^{\bar{N}}e^{-\theta_1 V - \theta_2 I}) = 1 - \prod_{r=1}^{k}\left(1 - \frac{\lambda\gamma_r}{\lambda + \theta_2}\right), \tag{66}$$

where $0 < z < 1$, $\theta_1 \geq 0$, $\theta_2 \geq 0$ and $\gamma_r = \gamma_r(z, \theta_1)$ $(r = 1, 2, \ldots, k)$.

PROOF. We use the result (56) with $(\theta_1, \theta_2, i\omega)$ replaced by $(\theta_1, 0, -\theta_2)$.
$\square$

Theorem 17. *For the queue $E_k/G/1$ we have the following:*

$$\sum_{0}^{\infty} z^n E(e^{i\omega_1 W_n + i\omega_2 \mathscr{I}_n}) = \frac{(\lambda - i\omega_2)^k}{(\lambda + i\omega_1)^k - z\lambda^k\phi_1(\omega_1)} \prod_{r=1}^{k}\left(\frac{\lambda - \lambda\xi_r + i\omega_1}{\lambda - \lambda\xi_r - i\omega_2}\right).$$

$$\lim_{n\to\infty} E(e^{i\omega W_n}) = \frac{k(1-\rho_1)i\omega}{(\lambda + i\omega)^k - \lambda^k\phi_1(\omega)} \prod_{r=1}^{k-1}\left(\frac{\lambda - \lambda\zeta_r + i\omega}{1-\zeta_r}\right) \quad (\rho_1 < 1).$$

$$\lim_{n\to\infty} E(e^{i\omega\mathscr{I}_n}) = (\lambda - i\omega)^k \prod_{r=1}^{k}\left(\frac{1-\zeta_r}{\lambda - \lambda\zeta_r - i\omega}\right) \quad (\rho_1 > 1).$$

---

[3] The distinction between strong and weak ladder epochs disappears in this case, as the distribution of X_n has a density.

Problems

1. Let v_z be the Lévy measure defined by (16) and

$$R_+(z, \omega) = \exp\left\{\int_0^\infty (e^{i\omega x} - 1) v_z(dx)\right\}$$

$$R_-(z, \omega) = \exp\left\{\int_{-\infty}^0 (e^{i\omega x} - 1) v_z(dx)\right\}.$$

Show that for fixed z in $(0, 1)$, $(1 - z)[1 - z\phi(\omega)]^{-1}$ is an infinitely divisible c.f., and

$$\frac{1 - z}{1 - z\phi(\omega)} = R_+(z, \omega) R_-(z, \omega),$$

the factorization being unique up to a factor of the form $e^{ia\omega}$, a being a real function of z.

2. Let $E|X_n| < \infty$ and $\alpha = E(X_n)$. Prove that

(i) if $\alpha > 0$, then $A < \infty$, $B = \infty$,
(ii) if $\alpha < 0$, then $A = \infty$, $B < \infty$, and
(iii) if $\alpha = 0$, and $P\{X_n = 0\} < 1$, then $A = \infty$, $B = \infty$.

3. Prove the following:

(i) If $A < \infty$, $B = \infty$, then with probability one,

$$\sup_{k \geq 0} S_k = +\infty, \qquad \lim_{n \to \infty} S_n = +\infty.$$

(ii) If $A = \infty$, $B < \infty$ and $P\{X_n = 0\} < 1$, then with probability one,

$$\sup_{k \geq 0} S_k < \infty, \qquad \lim_{n \to \infty} S_n = -\infty.$$

(iii) If $A = \infty$, $B = \infty$, then with probability one,

$$\sup_{k \geq 0} S_k = +\infty, \qquad \inf_{k \geq 0} S_k = -\infty.$$

4. Show that

$$(1 - z) \sum_0^\infty z^n E(e^{i\omega_1 W_n + i\omega_2 \mathcal{I}_n}) = R_+(z, \omega_1) R_-(z, -\omega_2),$$

where R_+ and R_- are defined in problem 1.

5. Show that

$$E(W_n) = \sum_1^n \frac{1}{m} E(S_m; S_m > 0),$$

$$E(\mathcal{I}_n) = \sum_1^n \frac{1}{m} E(-S_m; S_m \leq 0).$$

6. Show that the result (39) can be written as

$$\sum_0^\infty z^n E(e^{-\theta_1 C_n - \theta_2 \mathcal{B}_n}) = \{[1 - E(z^N e^{-\theta_1 V_N - \theta_2 U_N})][1 - E(z^{\bar{N}} e^{-\theta_1 U_{\bar{N}} - \theta_2 V_{\bar{N}}})]\}^{-1}.$$

Problems

7. Departures. Let $D_0 \equiv 0$, $D_{n+1} = U_n + W_n + v_{n+1}$ $(n \geq 0)$, so that $D_1, D_2, \ldots$ are the successive departure epochs. Also, let $d_n = D_n - D_{n-1}$ $(n \geq 1)$. Show that

$$E(d_n) \to a \quad \text{if } \alpha < 0,$$
$$\to b \quad \text{if } \alpha > 0,$$
$$\to a = b \quad \text{if } \alpha = 0 \text{ and } \sigma^2 < \infty.$$

8. Let $U(t)$ be the expected number of departures from the system. Prove the following:

(a) $\int_0^\infty e^{-\theta t} \, dU(t) = \dfrac{\psi_2(\theta)}{[1 - E(e^{-\theta V_N})][1 - E(e^{-\theta U_N})]}$, $(\theta > 0)$.

(b) As $t \to \infty$,

$$\frac{U(t)}{t} \to \frac{1}{a} \quad \text{if } \alpha < 0,$$
$$\to \frac{1}{b} \quad \text{if } \alpha > 0.$$

9. For the queue M/M/1 prove the result (51) for the busy period directly by using the Wiener–Hopf techniques of section 6 of the preceding chapter.

10. For the queue G/M/1 prove (with notation as in Problem 8) that

$$\int_0^\infty e^{-\theta t} \, dU(t) = \frac{E(e^{-\theta V_N})}{1 - \psi(\theta)} \quad (\theta > 0).$$

11. For the queue $G/E_k/1$ show that

$$(1-z) \sum_0^\infty z^n E(e^{i\omega W_n}) = 1 - \sum_1^k A_r e^{-(\lambda - \lambda \xi_r)x},$$

where

$$A_r = \xi_r^k \prod_{p \neq r} \left(\frac{1 - \xi_p}{\xi_r - \xi_p} \right) \quad (r = 1, 2, \ldots, k).$$

The limit distribution of W_n thus appears as the weighted sum of exponential distributions.

References

Andersen, Sparre E. (1953a): On sums of symmetrically dependent random variables. *Skan. Aktuar.* **36**, 123–138.

Andersen, Sparre E. (1953b): On the fluctuations of sums of random variables I. *Math. Scand.* **1**, 263–285.

Andersen, Sparre E. (1954): On the fluctuations of sums of random variables II. *Math. Scand.* **2**, 195–223.

Baxter, Glen (1958): An operator identity, *Pacific J. Math.* **8**, 649–663.

Beneš, V. E. (1957): On queues with Poisson arrivals. *Ann. Math. Statist.* **28**, 670–677.

Blackwell, D. (1953): Extension of a renewal theorem. *Pacific J. Math.* **3**, 315–320.

Erdös, P. and Kac, M. (1946): On certain limit theorems of the theory of probability. *Bull. Amer. Math. Soc.* **52**, 292–302.

Feller, W. (1959): On combinatorial methods in fluctuation theory. *The Harold Cramér Volume*, 75–91, John Wiley, New York.

Feller, W. (1971): *An Introduction to Probability Theory and Its Applications*, Volume 2, 3rd edition. John Wiley, New York.

Heyde, C. C. (1967): A limit theorem for random walks with drift. *J. Appl. Prob.* **4**, 144–150.

Kemperman, J. H. B. (1961): *The First Passage Problem for a Stationary Markov Chain*. University of Chicago Press, Chicago.

Kendall, D. G. (1957): Some problems in the theory of dams. *J. Roy. Stat. Soc.*, **B19**, 207–212.

Krein, M. G. (1958): Integral equations on a half-line with kernel depending upon the difference of the arguments. *Uspekhi Mat. Nauk* **13**, 3–120 [*Amer. Math. Soc. Translations Series* 2, **22**, 163–288].

Lindley, D. V. (1952): Theory of queues with a single server. *Proc. Camb. Phil. Soc.* **48**, 277–289.

Prabhu, N. U. (1970): Limit theorems for the single server queue with traffic intensity one: *J. Appl. Prob.* **7**, 227–233.

Smith, W. L. (1953): On the distribution of queueing times. *Proc. Camb. Phil. Soc.* **49**, 449–461.

Spitzer, F. (1956): A combinatorial lemma and its applications to probability theory. *Trans. Amer. Math. Soc.* **82**, 323–339.

Spitzer, F. (1957): The Wiener–Hopf equation whose kernel is a probability density. *Duke Math. J.* **24**, 327–344.

Spitzer, F. (1960a): The Wiener–Hopf equation whose kernel is a probability density II. *Duke Math. J.* **27**, 363–372.

Spitzer, F. (1960b): A Tauberian theorem and its probability interpretation. *Trans. Amer. Math. Soc.* **94**, 150–160.

PART II

CONTINUOUS TIME STORAGE MODELS

The theory of continuous time storage models was initiated by P. A. P. Moran, J. Gani and the author during 1956–63. They considered a model in which the input $X(t)$ is a Lévy process and the output is continuous and at a unit rate except when the store is empty. In spite of its simplicity the concepts underlying this model and the techniques used in its analysis are applicable in a wide variety of situations, for example, in insurance risk and queueing systems with first come, first served discipline or priority disciplines of the static or dynamic type. Recent results in the fluctuation theory of Lévy processes have led to the formulation and analysis of new storage models and also to a more elegant treatment of older models.

Chapter 3

The Basic Storage Model

1 Orientation

The models described in this chapter give rise to continuous time stochastic processes that are analogous to sums of independent and identically distributed random variables. We begin by describing models for two apparently different situations.

1.1 The Single-Server Queue with Poisson Arrivals

Consider the single-server queueing system M/G/1, in which customers arrive in a Poisson process with parameter λ $(0 < \lambda < \infty)$, and are served on a first-come, first-served basis. We assume that the service times of customers are independent random variables with a common d.f. $B(x)$ $(0 < x < \infty)$, which are also independent of the arrival process. Let us observe the system from the server's point of view and consider the amount of work that he is called upon to do from time to time. Let us denote by $X(t)$ the workload that is submitted to the server in a time interval $(0, t]$; that is, $X(t)$ is the amount of time that he is asked to work in order that he may serve all customers who arrive during $(0, t]$. We assume that $X(0) \equiv 0$. Then clearly, for $t > 0$,

$$X(t) = v_1 + v_2 + \cdots + v_{A(t)}, \tag{1}$$

where $A(t)$ is the total number of arrivals in $(0, t]$ and $v_1, v_2, \ldots$ are their successive service times. By our assumption $A(t)$ is a simple Poisson process with parameter λ and therefore the d.f. of $X(t)$ is given by

$$K(x, t) = P\{X(t) \le x\} = \sum_{n=0}^{\infty} e^{-\lambda t} \frac{(\lambda t)^n}{n!} B_n(x). \tag{2}$$

67

We shall call $\{X(t), t \geq 0\}$ the *input process*. We have

$$EX(t) = \lambda bt, \quad \text{Var } X(t) = \lambda ct, \qquad (3)$$

where

$$b = \int_0^\infty x \, dB(x), \quad c = \int_0^\infty x^2 \, dB(x), \qquad (4)$$

both moments being assumed finite. The d.f. (2) is the so-called compound Poisson.

The server works continuously at a unit rate except when the system is empty. At any time t, let $W(t)$ denote his *remaining workload* (or simply, workload). If the server has been busy throughout the interval $(0, t]$, then $W(t) = W(0) + X(t) - t$. This simple relation does not, however, prevail in the general situation.

1.2 Insurance Risk

The theory of insurance risk deals with the business of an insurance company, which is subject to the following assumptions:

(i) The number of claims arising in a time interval $(0, t]$ has a Poisson distribution with parameter λ $(0 < \lambda < \infty)$.
(ii) The amounts of successive claims are independent random variables with a common d.f. $P(x)$ $(-\infty < x < \infty)$, negative claims occurring in the case of ordinary whole-life annuities.

Under the assumptions (i) and (ii) it follows that the total amount $X(t)$ of claims arising in $(0, t]$ has the compound Poisson distribution

$$K(x, t) = \sum_{n=0}^{\infty} e^{-\lambda t} \frac{(\lambda t)^n}{n!} P_n(x). \qquad (5)$$

The expected claim during $(0, t]$ given by $\lambda \alpha t$, where

$$\alpha = \int_{-\infty}^{\infty} x \, dP(x) \quad (-\infty < \alpha < \infty); \qquad (6)$$

$\lambda \alpha$ is called the *net risk premium* rate (assumed finite).

(iii) From the totality of its policyholders the company receives premiums at a constant rate β $(-\infty < \beta < \infty)$. We call β the *gross risk premium* rate.

The difference $\beta - \lambda\alpha$ is called *safety loading*, which is in practice positive. However, we shall not assume this, but only that β and α are of the same sign. The ratio $\rho = \beta(\lambda\alpha)^{-1}$ (> 0) is called Lundberg's security factor and is of great importance in the theory.

The company's reserve fund at time t is given by

$$Z(t) = x + \beta t - X(t) \qquad (7)$$

with initial value $Z(0) = x \geq 0$. Here $Z(t)$ may assume positive or negative values, but the company is interested in choosing the initial reserve large enough to "avoid ruin" over a finite or an infinite horizon.

In the two models described above we saw that the basic process is the compound Poisson. An important feature of the models is that in any finite interval of time only a finite number of events occur (namely, customers' arrivals or claims). The resulting property of the basic process is that its sample functions take only a finite number of jumps in each finite interval, the total magnitude of these jumps being also finite. However, this description of the input is unrealistic in certain other situations. For example in the case of a dam it is very likely (roughly speaking) that there is a steady inflow of water, consisting of small as well as large amounts, there being more inflows of small amounts than large ones. To formulate this type of input precisely we need to consider the class of processes of which the compound Poisson is a special member, namely Lévy processes.

2 Lévy Processes

A process $\{X(t), t \geq 0\}$ is called a process with *stationary independent increments* if it satisfies the following properties:

(i) For $0 \leq t_1 < t_2 < \cdots < t_n$ ($n \geq 2$) the random variables

$$X(t_1), \ X(t_2) - X(t_1), \ X(t_3) - X(t_2), \ \ldots, \ X(t_n) - X(t_{n-1})$$

are independent.

(ii) The distribution of the increment $X(t_p) - X(t_{p-1})$ depends only on the difference $t_p - t_{p-1}$.

For such a process we can take $X(0) \equiv 0$ without loss of generality. For if $X(0) \neq 0$, then the process $Y(t) = X(t) - X(0)$ has stationary independent increments, and $Y(0) \equiv 0$.

If we write

$$X(t) = \sum_{k=1}^{n} \left[X\left(\frac{k}{n} t\right) - X\left(\frac{k-1}{n} t\right) \right], \tag{8}$$

then $X(t)$ is seen to be the sum of n independent random variables all of which are distributed as $X(t/n)$. Thus a process with stationary independent increments is the generalization to continuous time of sums of independent and identically distributed random variables. Since (8) is true for all $n \geq 1$ it follows that $X(t)$ has an infinitely divisible distribution.

A *Lévy process* is a process with stationary independent increments which satisfies the following additional conditions:

(iii) $X(t)$ is continuous in probability. That is, for each $\varepsilon > 0$
$$P\{|X(t)| > \varepsilon\} \to 0 \quad \text{as} \quad t \to 0+.$$

(iv) There exist left and right limits $X(t-)$ and $X(t+)$ and we assume that $X(t)$ is right continuous: that is, $X(t+) = X(t)$.

[The quantity $X(t) - X(t-)$ is called the *jump* of the process at time t.]

Under the regularity conditions (iii) and (iv) it can be proved that the c.f. of $X(t)$ is given by

$$E[e^{i\omega X(t)}] = e^{-t\phi(\omega)} \qquad (i = \sqrt{-1}, \omega \text{ real}), \tag{9}$$

where

$$\phi(\omega) = i\omega a - \int_{-\infty}^{\infty} \frac{e^{i\omega x} - 1 - i\omega\tau(x)}{x^2} M(dx), \tag{10}$$

a being a real constant, $\tau(x)$ a centering function given by

$$\begin{aligned}\tau(x) &= -1 \quad \text{for } x < -1, \\ &= x \quad \text{for } |x| \le 1, \\ &= +1 \quad \text{for } x > 1,\end{aligned} \tag{11}$$

and M a canonical measure: $M\{I\} < \infty$ for each bounded interval I, and

$$M^+(x) = \int_{x-}^{\infty} \frac{1}{y^2} M(dy) < \infty, \qquad M^-(-x) = \int_{-\infty}^{-x+} \frac{1}{y^2} M(dy) < \infty. \tag{12}$$

for each $x > 0$.

EXAMPLE 1. Suppose that the measure M is concentrated at the origin with $M\{0\} = \sigma^2 > 0$. Then $\phi(\omega) = i\omega a + \frac{1}{2}\omega^2\sigma^2$ and

$$E[e^{i\omega X(t)}] = e^{-i\omega at - (1/2)\omega^2\sigma^2 t}.$$

This shows that in this case $X(t)$ is the *Brownian motion* with a drift.

EXAMPLE 2. Suppose that M has no atom at the origin and

$$\lambda = \int_{-\infty}^{\infty} \frac{1}{x^2} M(dx) < \infty.$$

We can then write

$$M^+(x) = \lambda[1 - B(x-)], \qquad M^-(-x) = \lambda B(-x) \qquad (x > 0),$$

where $B(x)$ is a distribution function. Thus we can simplify (10) and write

$$\phi(\omega) = -i\omega d - \lambda \int_{-\infty}^{\infty} (e^{i\omega x} - 1) \, dB(x).$$

2 Lévy Processes

This yields the result

$$E[e^{i\omega X(t)}] = e^{i\omega dt - \lambda t[1 - \psi(\omega)]},$$

where $\psi(\omega)$ is the c.f. of $B(x)$. The process $X(t)$ is clearly a *compound Poisson*.

The probabilistic interpretation of the measure M is the following. If $M\{0\} = \sigma^2 > 0$ then $X(t)$ has a Brownian motion component. Let $N_+(t, x)$ denote the number of jumps of magnitude $\geq x > 0$ and $N_-(t, x)$ the number of jumps of magnitude $\leq x < 0$ occurring in a time interval $(0, t]$. Then $N_+(t, x)$ and $N_-(t, x)$ are Poisson processes with parameters $M^+(x)$ and $M^-(x)$ respectively. The total number of positive jumps in $(0, t]$ is a Poisson process with parameter $M^+(0)$ and thus in each finite interval there are a finite or infinite number of positive jumps according as $M^+(0) < \infty$ or $= \infty$. A similar statement holds for the total number of negative jumps.

The process $X(t)$ is of *bounded variation* if and only if $M\{0\} = 0$ and moreover,

$$\int_{|x|<1} \frac{1}{|x|} M(dx) < \infty. \tag{13}$$

In this case we can write

$$\phi(\omega) = -i\omega d - \int_{0+}^{\infty} \frac{e^{i\omega x} - 1}{x^2} M(dx) - \int_{-\infty}^{0-} \frac{e^{i\omega x} - 1}{x^2} M(dx) \tag{14}$$

and call the constant d the *drift* of the process. A process with bounded variation is therefore of the form

$$X(t) = dt + X_1(t) - X_2(t), \tag{15}$$

where $X_1(t)$ and $X_2(t)$ are processes whose sample functions are non-negative.

A Continuous Time Model for a Dam. Consider a dam (water reservoir) of large enough (effectively infinite) capacity, and let $X(t)$ denote the input of water into it during a time interval $(0, t]$. Our description of a process with stationary independent increments based on the properties (i) and (ii) mentioned earlier is in agreement with our intuitive concept of inputs into the dam. It is also natural to impose the regularity conditions (iii) and (iv) on the input process. Thus we assume that $\{X(t), t \geq 0\}$ is a Lévy process. Remembering that $X(t) \geq 0$ it follows from the above results that the c.f. of $X(t)$ is given by $e^{-t\phi(\omega)}$, where

$$\phi(\omega) = \int_{0+}^{\infty} (e^{i\omega x} - 1)x^{-2} M(dx), \tag{16}$$

with $M^+(0) = \int_{0+}^{\infty} x^{-2} M(dx) = \infty$. Let the release from the dam be continuous and at a unit rate except when the dam is empty. If $Z(t)$ denotes the content of the dam at time t, then $Z(t) = Z(0) + X(t) - t$ if the dam remains wet throughout the interval $(0, t]$.

To illustrate the concept of inputs into the dam we consider the following.

EXAMPLE 3. Let $M(dx) = e^{-x/\rho} x\, dx$ $(0 < x < \infty, 0 < \rho < \infty)$. We have then

$$\phi(\omega) = \int_0^\infty (e^{i\omega x} - 1)e^{-x/\rho}\frac{dx}{x} = -\log(1 - i\omega\rho)$$

and

$$E[e^{i\omega X(t)}] = (1 - i\omega\rho)^{-t}.$$

This shows that $X(t)$ has the gamma density

$$k(x, t) = e^{-x/\rho} \rho^{-t} \frac{x^{t-1}}{\Gamma(t)} \qquad (x > 0, t > 0).$$

Note that

$$M^+(0) = \int_0^\infty e^{-x/\rho} \frac{dx}{x} = \infty.$$

Remarks. (a) Other possible centering functions that can be used in (10) are

$$\tau(x) = \sin x \quad \text{and} \quad \tau(x) = \frac{x}{1 + x^2}.$$

(b) The measure v defined by

$$v\{0\} = 0, \qquad v(dx) = x^{-2} M(dx) \qquad (x \neq 0),$$

is called a Lévy measure. We have

$$\int_{-\infty}^\infty \min(1, x^2) v(dx) < \infty,$$

as can be easily verified from (12).

(c) Let

$$M(t) = \sup_{0 \le \tau \le t} X(\tau), \qquad m(t) = \inf_{0 \le \tau \le t} X(\tau). \qquad (17)$$

On account of our assumptions on $X(t)$, the functionals $M(t)$ and $m(t)$ are both random variables. The following result will be useful in simplifying some calculations.

Lemma 1. *For any Lévy process $X(t)$ we have*

$$\{M(t), M(t) - X(t)\} \sim \{X(t) - m(t), -m(t)\}. \qquad (18)$$

PROOF. For $0 \leq \tau \leq t$, let $X_1(\tau) = X(t) - X(t - \tau)$. Then $X_1(\tau) \sim X(\tau)$ and

$$\{X(t) - m(t), -m(t)\} = \left\{ \sup_{0 \leq \tau \leq t} [X(t) - X(\tau)], - \inf_{0 \leq \tau \leq t} X(\tau) \right\}$$

$$= \left\{ \sup_{0 \leq \tau \leq t} X_1(t - \tau), - \inf_{0 \leq \tau \leq t} [X_1(t) - X_1(t - \tau)] \right\}$$

$$\sim \left\{ \sup_{0 \leq \tau \leq t} X(\tau), - \inf_{0 \leq \tau \leq t} [X(t) - X(t - \tau)] \right\}$$

$$= \{M(t), M(t) - X(t)\}. \qquad \square$$

3 A Generalized Storage Model

Our discussion of the M/G/1 queue in section 1 and the dam model in section 2 motivates us to formulate a storage model by defining the storage level at time t to be $Z(t)$, where

$$Z(t) = Z(0) + Y(t) + \int_0^t \chi_{Z(s)} \, ds \qquad (t \geq 0) \qquad (19)$$

with $Z(0) \geq 0$,

$$\begin{aligned} \chi_{Z(t)} &= 0 \quad \text{if } Z(t) > 0, \\ &= 1 \quad \text{if } Z(t) = 0, \end{aligned} \qquad (20)$$

and $Y(t) = X(t) - t$, $X(t)$ being a Lévy process with nondecreasing sample functions and with zero drift. We take $X(0) \equiv 0$. The Laplace transform (L.T.) of $X(t)$ is given by $E e^{-\theta X(t)} = e^{-t\phi(\theta)}$, where

$$\phi(\theta) = \int_0^\infty (1 - e^{-\theta x}) x^{-2} M(dx) \qquad (\theta > 0) \qquad (21)$$

with $M^+(0) \leq \infty$. Let us denote

$$\rho = \int_0^\infty \frac{1}{x} M(dx) \leq \infty, \qquad \sigma^2 = \int_0^\infty M(dx) \leq \infty; \qquad (22)$$

then $EX(t) = \rho t$ and $\text{Var } X(t) = \sigma^2 t$. The *net input* process $Y(t)$ is also a Lévy process, with drift -1.

We note that in the M/G/1 queue $Z(t)$ is identical with $W(t)$, the remaining workload at time t, while in the dam model $Z(t)$ is the content of the dam at time t. The equation (19) is a stochastic integral equation for $Z(t)$. We prove below that it has a unique solution. We are also able to evaluate the integral

$$I(t) = \int_0^t \chi_{Z(s)} \, ds. \qquad (23)$$

It is clear that $I(t)$ is the duration of time that the store has remained empty in the time interval $(0, t]$. It will turn out that $Z(t)$ and $I(t)$ are related to the functionals

$$M(t) = \sup_{0 \le \tau \le t} Y(\tau), \quad m(t) = \inf_{0 \le \tau \le t} Y(\tau). \tag{24}$$

We need the following result; for proof see the Appendix.

Lemma 2. *The functional equation* $\eta = s + \phi(\eta)$ $(s > 0)$ *has a unique continuous solution* $\eta \equiv \eta(s)$ *with* $\eta(\infty) = \infty$. *Furthermore*:

(i) *as* $s \to 0+$, $\eta(s) \to \eta_0$, *where* η_0 *is the largest positive root of the equation* $\eta_0 = \phi(\eta_0)$, *and* $\eta_0 > 0$ *iff* $\rho > 1$;
(ii) $\eta'(0+) = (1-\rho)^{-1}$ *if* $\rho < 1$, *and* $= \infty$ *if* $\rho = 1$.

EXAMPLE 1. In the queueing model M/G/1 described in section 1, we have already seen that the input $X(t)$ is a compound Poisson process. From (2) we find that

$$Ee^{-\theta X(t)} = e^{-\lambda t[1-\psi(\theta)]} \quad (\theta > 0) \tag{25}$$

where $\psi(\theta)$ is the L.T. of the service time d.f. $B(x)$. Thus $\phi(\theta) = \lambda - \lambda\psi(\theta)$. Consider the special case of the M/M/1 queue, where $B(x) = 1 - e^{-\mu x}$ and $\psi(\theta) = \mu(\mu + \theta)^{-1}$. The equation $\eta = s + \phi(\eta)$ reduces in this case to

$$\eta^2 - (s + \lambda - \mu)\eta - \mu s = 0.$$

The root $\eta \equiv \eta(s)$ of this quadratic equation, with $\eta(\infty) = \infty$ is found to be

$$\eta = \frac{(s + \lambda - \mu) + \sqrt{(s + \lambda - \mu)^2 + 4\mu s}}{2} \quad (s > 0). \tag{26}$$

We have

$$\eta(0+) = \frac{(\lambda - \mu) + |\lambda - \mu|}{2} = \lambda - \mu \quad \text{if } \lambda > \mu,$$
$$= 0 \quad \text{if } \lambda \le \mu. \tag{27}$$

EXAMPLE 2. Let us consider a dam model with input process $X(t)$ having the density

$$k(x, t) = \frac{t}{\sqrt{2\pi x^3}} e^{-t^2/2x} \quad (0 < x < \infty, 0 < t < \infty) \tag{28}$$

(stable density with exponent $\frac{1}{2}$). It is known that

$$Ee^{-\theta X(t)} = \int_0^\infty e^{-\theta x} k(x, t)\, dx = e^{-t\sqrt{2\theta}} \quad (\theta > 0). \tag{29}$$

3 A Generalized Storage Model

From (29) it follows that all moments of $X(t)$ are infinite. Here $\phi(\theta) = \sqrt{2\theta}$ and we have to solve the equation $\eta = s + \sqrt{2\eta}$. The substitution $2\eta = x^2$ reduces this to the quadratic equation $x^2 - 2x - 2s = 0$ and it is found that the appropriate root of this is $x = 1 + \sqrt{1 + 2s}$. Therefore

$$\eta = 1 + s + \sqrt{1 + 2s} \qquad (s > 0) \tag{30}$$

is the desired solution, and $\eta(0+) = 2$.

Theorem 1. *The integral equation (19) has the unique solution*

$$Z(t) = Z(0) + Y(t) + I(t), \tag{31}$$

where

$$I(t) = \max\{0, -m(t) - Z(0)\}. \tag{32}$$

PROOF. From (19) we obtain

$$Z(t) = Z(\tau-) + Y(t) - Y(\tau-) + \int_{\tau-}^{t} \chi_{Z(s)} \, ds$$

$$\geq Y(t) - Y(\tau-) \qquad (\tau \leq t).$$

Furthermore, let $t_0 = \max\{\tau : \tau \leq t, Z(\tau-) = 0\}$ if the set in brackets is nonempty. Then t_0 is the last epoch in $(0, t]$ at which the store was empty, and

$$Z(t) = Y(t) - Y(t_0-).$$

Denoting $f(\tau) = Y(t) - Y(\tau-)$ $(0 \leq \tau \leq t)$ we therefore see that $Z(t)$ is an upper bound of the function $f(\tau)$, and $f(t_0) = Z(t)$. Thus

$$Z(t) = \sup_{0 \leq \tau \leq t} f(\tau) = \sup_{0 \leq \tau \leq t} [Y(t) - Y(\tau-)]. \tag{33}$$

If during $(0, t]$ the store is never empty (which implies $Z(0) > 0$) then from (19) we have $Z(0) + Y(\tau-) > 0$ and $Z(t) = Z(0) + Y(t) > f(\tau)$ $(0 \leq \tau \leq t)$. A comparison with (33) shows that quite generally

$$Z(t) = \max\left\{\sup_{0 \leq \tau \leq t}[Y(t) - Y(\tau-)], Z(0) + Y(t)\right\} \tag{34}$$

$$= \max\{Y(t) - m(t), Z(0) + Y(t)\}.$$

From (20) it follows that

$$I(t) = \int_0^t \chi_{Z(s)} \, ds = Z(t) - Z(0) - Y(t)$$

$$= \max\{-m(t) - Z(0), 0\},$$

as required. The proof is therefore completed. □

Theorem 2. *We have*

$$\int_0^\infty e^{-st} E\{e^{-\theta_1 Z(t) - \theta_2 I(t)} | Z(0) = x\} \, dt = \frac{e^{-\theta_1 x} - (\theta_1 + \theta_2) J^*(\theta_2, s)}{s - \theta_1 + \phi(\theta_1)} \quad (35)$$

$$(\theta_1 > 0, \theta_2 > 0, s > 0),$$

where $J^*(\theta_2, s) = e^{-x\eta}(\theta_2 + \eta)^{-1}$, $\eta \equiv \eta(s)$ *being given by Lemma* 1.

PROOF. Let $\zeta(t) = \chi_{Z(t)}$, so that $I(t) = \int_0^t \zeta(\tau) \, d\tau$. We have

$$\int_0^t e^{-\theta I(\tau)} \, dI(\tau) = \left[-\frac{1}{\theta} e^{-\theta I(\tau)} \right]_0^t = \frac{1 - e^{-\theta I(t)}}{\theta},$$

so that

$$e^{-\theta I(t)} = 1 - \theta \int_0^t e^{-\theta I(\tau)} \, dI(\tau)$$

$$= 1 - \theta \int_0^t e^{-\theta I(\tau)} \zeta(\tau) \, d\tau \quad (\theta > 0).$$

Using this relation we find that

$$e^{-\theta_1 Z(t) - \theta_2 I(t)} = e^{-\theta_1 [Z(0) + Y(t) + I(t)] - \theta_2 I(t)}$$

$$= e^{-\theta_1 [Z(0) + Y(t)]} \cdot e^{-(\theta_1 + \theta_2) I(t)}$$

$$= e^{-\theta_1 [Z(0) + Y(t)]} \left\{ 1 - (\theta_1 + \theta_2) \int_0^t e^{-(\theta_1 + \theta_2) I(\tau)} \zeta(\tau) \, d\tau \right\}$$

$$= e^{-\theta_1 [Z(0) + Y(t)]} - (\theta_1 + \theta_2) \int_0^t e^{-\theta_1 [Y(t) - Y(\tau)] - \theta_1 Z(\tau) - \theta_2 I(\tau)} \zeta(\tau) \, d\tau.$$

Since $\zeta(\tau) > 0$ iff $Z(\tau) = 0$ we can rewrite this as

$$e^{-\theta_1 Z(t) - \theta_2 I(t)} = e^{-\theta_1 [Z(0) + Y(t)]} - (\theta_1 + \theta_2) \int_0^t e^{-\theta_1 [Y(t) - Y(\tau)] - \theta_2 I(\tau)} \zeta(\tau) \, d\tau. \quad (36)$$

Taking expectations of both sides of (36) and noting that $\{I(\tau), \zeta(\tau)\}$ depends only on $Y(\tau')$ ($0 \le \tau' \le \tau$) and not on $Y(t) - Y(\tau)$ we obtain

$$E\{e^{-\theta_1 Z(t) - \theta_2 I(t)} | Z(0) = x\}$$

$$= e^{-\theta_1 x - t[\phi(\theta_1) - \theta_1]} - (\theta_1 + \theta_2) \int_0^t e^{-(t - \tau)[\phi(\theta_1) - \theta_1]} J(\theta_2, \tau) \, d\tau, \quad (37)$$

where $J(\theta_2, t) = E[e^{-\theta_2 I(t)} \zeta(t)]$. Let $J^*(\theta_2, s) = \int_0^\infty e^{-st} J(\theta_2, t) \, dt$. Then (37) leads to the result (35), but it remains to evaluate the transform $J^*(\theta_2, s)$. By Lemma 2 for fixed $s > 0$ the denominator in (35) vanishes for $\theta_1 = \eta$, this η being unique. Since the left side of (35) is a bounded analytic function of θ_1, θ_2, s the numerator in (35) must also vanish for $\theta_1 = \eta$. This yields the desired result for $J^*(\theta_2, s)$ and the theorem is completely proved. □

3 A Generalized Storage Model

Corollary 1. *For $\theta > 0$, $s > 0$ we have*

$$\int_0^\infty e^{-st} E[e^{-\theta I(t)} \mid Z(0) = x] \, dt = \frac{1}{s}\left(1 - e^{-x\eta}\frac{\theta}{\theta + \eta}\right), \tag{38}$$

$$\int_0^\infty e^{-st} E[e^{-\theta Z(t)} \mid Z(0) = x] \, dt = \frac{e^{-\theta x} - \theta F_x^*(0, s)}{s - \theta + \phi(\theta)}, \tag{39}$$

where $F_x^*(0, s) = e^{-x\eta} \eta^{-1}$, $\eta \equiv \eta(s)$ being given by Lemma 1.

PROOF. The result (38) follows from (35) by setting $\theta_1 = 0$, $\theta_2 = \theta$. The result (39) follows from (35) in a similar manner, but we should note that $J(0, t) = E[\zeta(t)] = F_x(0, t) = P\{Z(t) = 0 \mid Z(0) = x\}$, so that

$$F_x^*(0, s) = \int_0^\infty e^{-st} F_x(0, t) \, dt = J^*(0, s) = e^{-x\eta} \eta^{-1}. \tag{40}$$

$\square$

If $Z(0) = 0$ then Theorem 1 states that

$$I(t) = -m(t), \qquad Z(t) = \sup_{0 \leq \tau \leq t} [Y(t) - Y(\tau-)] \tag{41}$$

with probability one. From Lemma 1, we find that

$$Z(t) \sim M(t), \qquad Z(0) = 0. \tag{42}$$

Corollary 1 is thus concerned with the distribution of $M(t)$ and $m(t)$, which are the supremum and infimum functionals of the Lévy process $Y(t)$. Since M and m are monotone in t the limit behavior of our processes $I(t)$ and $Z(t)$ follows directly from Corollary 1. The following results, however, hold for $Z(0) = x \geq 0$. $\square$

Theorem 3. *Let $Z(0) = x \geq 0$. Then with probability one $I(t) \to I \leq \infty$. If $\rho \leq 1$, $I = \infty$ with probability one, while if $\rho > 1$, the random variable I has the d.f.*

$$P\{I \leq y\} = 1 - e^{-(x+y)\eta_0} \qquad (y \geq 0), \tag{43}$$

with $\eta_0 > 0$ given by Lemma 2.

PROOF. From (23) it follows that $I(t)$ is a monotone nondecreasing function of t, and so with probability one $I(t) \to I \leq \infty$. Therefore $E[e^{-\theta I(t)}] \to E(e^{-\theta I})$, where by a Tauberian theorem

$$E(e^{-\theta I}) = \lim_{s \to 0+} s \int_0^\infty e^{-st} E[e^{-\theta I(t)}] \, dt$$

$$= 1 - \lim_{s \to 0+} e^{-x\eta} \cdot \frac{\theta}{\theta + \eta}$$

$$= 0 \qquad \qquad \text{if } \rho \leq 1$$

$$= 1 - e^{-x\eta_0} \frac{\theta}{\theta + \eta_0} \qquad \text{if } \rho > 1.$$

The desired results now follow immediately. □

Theorem 4. *Let $Z(0) = x \geq 0$. Then as $t \to \infty$, $Z(t) \to \infty$ in distribution if $\rho \geq 1$, and otherwise converges in distribution to a random variable Z with the transform*

$$E(e^{-\theta Z}) = \frac{(1-\rho)\theta}{\theta - \phi(\theta)} \qquad (\theta > 0). \tag{44}$$

PROOF. (i) Let $Z(0) = 0$; then as already shown in (42), $Z(t) \sim M(t)$. Since $M(t)$ is a monotone nondecreasing function of t, $M(t) \to M \leq \infty$ as $t \to \infty$. It follows that $Z(t)$ converges in distribution to the random variable M. Therefore $E[e^{-\theta Z(t)}] \to E(e^{-\theta M})$, where by a Tauberian theorem

$$E(e^{-\theta M}) = \lim_{s \to 0+} s \int_0^\infty e^{-st} E[e^{-\theta Z(t)} | Z(0) = 0] \, dt$$

$$= \frac{\theta}{\theta - \phi(\theta)} \cdot \lim_{s \to 0+} sF^*(0, s). \tag{45}$$

Using Lemma 2 in (40) we find that

$$\lim_{t \to \infty} F(0, t) = \lim_{s \to 0+} sF^*(0, s) = \lim_{s \to 0+} \frac{s}{\eta(s)}$$

$$= 0 \qquad \text{if } \rho \geq 1, \tag{46}$$

$$= 1 - \rho \qquad \text{if } \rho < 1.$$

The desired result now follows from (45) and (46), except that we have changed the notation from M to Z.

(ii) Let $Z(0) = x \geq 0$, and write $Z_x(t)$, $I_x(t)$ to denote the random variables $Z(t)$, $I(t)$. Then from Theorem 1 we find that

$$Z_x(t) = Z_0(t) + L_x(t), \tag{47}$$

where $L_x(t) = \max\{0, x + m(t)\}$. Since $Z_x(t) \geq Z_0(t)$ it follows that if $Z_0(t) \to \infty$ in distribution, so does $Z_x(t)$. This happens iff $\rho \geq 1$. It remains to show that if $\rho < 1$, $Z_x(t)$ and $Z_0(t)$ have the same limit distribution. In order to do this we note that $L_x(t)$ is a monotone nonincreasing function of t, and $0 \leq L_x(t) \leq x$. Therefore as $t \to \infty$, $L_x(t) \to L_x$ where $0 \leq L_x \leq x$. Now

$$P\{L_x(t) \leq y\} = P\{x + m(t) \leq y\}$$

$$= P\{I_0(t) \geq x - y\} \qquad (0 \leq y \leq x).$$

From Theorem 3 it follows that this last probability converges to 1 if $\rho < 1$, so in this case $L_x \equiv 0$ and the desired result follows. The theorem is thus completely proved. □

4 A First Passage Time

For the storage model formulated in the last section we define the random variable T as follows:

$$T = \inf\{t: Z(t) = 0\}, \quad Z(0) > 0. \tag{48}$$

If our model describes the M/G/1 queue of section 1 we shall call T the *busy period* initiated by a workload $W(0)$, and if it describes the continuous time model of section 2, then we shall call T the *wet period* initiated by a water level $Z(0)$. From (19) it is clear that T has the same distribution as the random variable

$$T(x) = \inf\{t: Y(t) \leq -x\} \quad (x > 0). \tag{49}$$

Here $T(x)$ is the first passage time of the Lévy process $Y(t)$ into the set $(-\infty, -x]$. For completeness we define $T(0) \equiv 0$.

Theorem 5. *Let $T(x)$ be the random variable defined by (49) and assume that $T(x) \to 0$ as $x \to 0+$. Then we have the following:*

(i) $E[e^{-sT(x)}] = e^{-x\eta} \ (s > 0)$;
(ii) $P\{T(x) < \infty\} = 1$ if $\rho \leq 1$, and $= e^{-x\eta_0}$ if $\rho > 1$;
(iii) If $\rho < 1$, $E[T(x)] = x(1-\rho)^{-1}$, $\text{Var}[T(x)] = x\sigma^2(1-\rho)^{-3}$;
(iv) If $\rho = 1$, $E[T(x)] = \infty$;

where $\eta \equiv \eta(s)$ and $\eta_0 = \eta(0+)$ are given by Lemma 2.

PROOF. The results (ii)–(iv) follow in the usual manner from the L.T. of the distribution of $T(x)$, given by (i); so it suffices to prove (i). The proof rests on the following two properties:

(1) $T(x+y) - T(x)$ is independent of $T(x)$ and has the same distribution as $T(y)$;
(2) $T(x) \sim x + T[X(x)]$.

The first of these properties is a consequence of the fact that $Y(t)$ has drift -1 and a passage from 0 to $-x-y < 0$ can occur only after a passage to $-x < 0$. Independence of $T(x)$ and $T(x+y) - T(x)$ is a consequence of the strong Markov property of the Lévy process $Y(t)$. The second property readily follows from the definition.

It follows from (1) that $f(s; x) = E[e^{-sT(x)}]$ satisfies the property $f(s; x+y) = f(s; x)f(s; y)$. Using the fact that $f(s; x) \to 1$ as $x \to 0+$ we obtain the result that $f(s; x) = e^{x\eta}$. The property (2) now yields

$$e^{-x\eta} = e^{-sx}E[e^{-\eta X(x)}] = e^{-sx - \phi(\eta)x}.$$

Since this is true for all $x > 0$ it follows that the η in (i) is indeed the solution of the equation $\eta = s + \phi(\eta)$. The proof is therefore completed. □

4.1 Application to M/G/1 and Related Systems

(a) *The Busy Period in* M/G/1. We consider the queueing model M/G/1 described in section 1. As shown in Example 1 of section 3 we have $\phi(\theta) = \lambda - \lambda\psi(\theta)$ where $\psi(\theta)$ is the L.T. of the service time d.f. $B(x)$. It follows from Theorem 5(i) that the Laplace transform of the busy period $T(x)$ is given by $e^{-x\eta}$, where $\eta = \eta(s)$ is the unique continuous solution of the equation $\eta = s + \lambda - \lambda\psi(\eta)$, with $\eta(\infty) = \infty$.

At time $t = 0$ let us suppose that there are n (≥ 1) customers in the system and service is due to commence on the first of them. Let T_n be the busy period that follows. Clearly $T_n = T(v_1 + v_2 + \cdots + v_n)$, where $v_1, v_2, \ldots, v_n$ are the service times of these n customers. Therefore

$$E(e^{-sT_n}) = E[e^{-sT(v_1+v_2+\cdots+v_n)}]$$
$$= E[e^{-\eta(v_1+v_2+\cdots+v_n)}] = [\psi(\eta)]^n.$$

In particular T_1 is the conventionally defined busy period.

(b) *Balking.* Customers arrive in a Poisson process with parameter λ and join the queue with probability one if the server is free, and with probability p (< 1) otherwise. The service mechanism is as in (a) above. As long as the system is busy, the number of effective arrivals forms a Poisson process with parameter λp, and therefore $E[e^{-sT(x)}] = e^{-x\eta}$ where $\eta \equiv \eta_p(s)$ is the unique continuous solution of the equation $\eta = s + \lambda p - \lambda p\psi(\eta)$ with $\eta(\infty) = \infty$.

(c) *Batch Arrivals.* Customers arrive in a Poisson process of batches of random size having the distribution $\{c_n, n = 1, 2, \ldots\}$. The service time of each customer has the d.f. $B(x)$. Clearly, the input in this case is the compound Poisson process with L.T. $e^{-\lambda t\{1-C[\psi(\theta)]\}}$, where $C(s) = \sum_1^\infty c_n s^n$. It follows that $E[e^{-sT(x)}] = e^{-x\eta}$ where $\eta = \eta(s)$ is the unique continuous solution of the equation $\eta = s + \lambda - \lambda C[\psi(\eta)]$, with $\eta(\infty) = \infty$.

(d) *Modified Service Rule.* Suppose that in the M/G/1 system described in (a) above the customer who initiates a busy period has a service time with d.f. $B_0(x)$, while all others have service times with d.f. $B(x)$. For the busy period T_1 initiated by a single customer we have

$$E(e^{-sT_1}) = E[e^{-sT(v_1)}] = E[e^{-v_1\eta}] = \psi_0(\eta),$$

where ψ_0 is the L.T. of $B_0(x)$, and $\eta = \eta(s)$ is as defined in (a) above.

(e) "*Last come, first served*" *Discipline.* In the M/G/1 system described in (a) above, suppose we change the queue discipline to "last come, first served", with the provision of no pre-emption, that is, the customer at the counter will continue to receive service when a new customer arrives. Let

$\bar{W}(t)$ be the time a customer would have to wait for service if he arrived at time t. Then

$$\bar{W}(t) = 0 \quad \text{if the system is empty,}$$
$$= T[v(t)] \quad \text{otherwise,}$$

where $v(t)$ is the residual service time of the customer at the counter. From Theorem 5 we see that with positive probability we may have $\bar{W}(t) = \infty$ for finite t, that is, a customer arriving at time t will not ever reach the counter.

(f) *The Process* $\{T(x), x \geq 0\}$. Let us consider a continuous infinity of M/G/1 systems, and observe for each system the duration of its first busy period. Our observations will then yield a process $\{T(x), x \geq 0\}$. We have

$$T(x) = x + T_{A(x)},$$

where $A(x)$ is the number of arrivals during $(0, x]$. Therefore

$$P\{T(x) \leq t\} = \sum_{n=0}^{\infty} e^{-\lambda x} \frac{(\lambda x)^n}{n!} G_n(t - x) \quad (t \geq x \geq 0), \quad (50)$$

where $G_n(x)$ is the d.f. of T_n. The equation (50) shows that $T(x)$ is a compound Poisson process with unit drift, in which jumps occur at a rate λ and jump sizes have the same distribution as T_1.

4.2 Application to Dam Models

In applying Theorem 5 to the dam model of section 2, it is natural to assume that the input $X(t)$ has an absolutely continuous distribution. Note that in the queueing model M/G/1 we have $P\{X(t) = 0\} = e^{-\lambda t} > 0$, so that the input distribution is discontinuous. We have the following result.

Theorem 6. *If $X(t)$ has an absolutely continuous distribution with density $k(x, t)$, then the random variable $T(x)$ has also an absolutely continuous distribution with density $g(t, x)$, where*

$$g(t, x) = \frac{x}{t} k(t - x, t) \quad \text{for } t > x > 0, \quad (51)$$
$$= 0 \quad \text{otherwise.}$$

PROOF. Using (42) we obtain from Corollary 1

$$r_+(s, \omega) = s \int_0^\infty e^{-st} E[e^{i\omega M(t)}] \, dt = \frac{s}{\eta} \cdot \frac{\eta + i\omega}{s + \Phi(\omega)}, \quad (52)$$

$$r_-(s, \omega) = s \int_0^\infty e^{-st} E[e^{i\omega m(t)}] \, dt = \frac{\eta}{\eta + i\omega}, \quad (53)$$

where $M(t)$ and $m(t)$ are the supremum and infimum functionals of the net input process $Y(t)$ and $Ee^{i\omega Y(t)} = e^{-t\Phi(\omega)}$. We therefore have

$$\frac{s}{s + \Phi(\omega)} = r_+(s, \omega)r_-(s, \omega) \qquad (s > 0, \omega \text{ real}). \tag{54}$$

This identity is a Wiener–Hopf factorization for the Lévy process $Y(t)$ in the following sense. We have

$$\frac{s}{s + \Phi(\omega)} = \exp\left\{\log \frac{s}{s + \Phi(\omega)}\right\}$$

$$= \exp\left\{\int_0^\infty e^{-st} t^{-1} E[e^{i\omega Y(t)} - 1] \, dt\right\}$$

$$= \exp\left\{\int_{-\infty}^\infty (e^{i\omega x} - 1) v_s(dx)\right\},$$

where

$$v_s\{0\} = 0, \qquad v_s(dx) = \int_0^\infty e^{-st} t^{-1} k(t + x, t) \, dt \, dx \qquad (x \neq 0). \tag{55}$$

It can be proved that for fixed $s > 0$, v_s is a Lévy measure, so that the expression on the left side of (54) is an infinitely divisible c.f. It can also be proved that for fixed $s > 0$, $r_+(s, \omega)$ and $r_-(s, \omega)$ are also infinitely divisible c.f.'s of distributions concentrated on $(0, \infty)$ and $(-\infty, 0)$ respectively. Thus (54) is a Wiener–Hopf factorization of $s[s + \Phi(\omega)]^{-1}$, and this factorization is unique (up to a factor $e^{ia\omega}$, where a is a real function of s) if restricted to infinitely divisible c.f.'s on the right side of (54).

Now fixed $s > 0$, $\eta(\eta + i\omega)^{-1}$ is the c.f. of the exponential density on $(-\infty, 0)$, which is infinitely divisible and has Lévy measure with density $e^{\eta x}(-x)^{-1}$ $(x < 0)$. On account of the uniqueness of the factorization (54) we therefore have from (55),

$$\frac{e^{\eta x}}{(-x)} = \int_0^\infty e^{-st} t^{-1} k(t + x, t) \, dt \qquad (x < 0)$$

or

$$e^{-\eta x} = \int_0^\infty e^{-st} g(t, x) \, dt \qquad (x > 0). \tag{56}$$

Since $e^{-\eta x}$ is the L.T. of the random variable $T(x)$ it follows that $g(t, x)$ is the required density. □

EXAMPLE 1 (Example 2 of section 3). Suppose $X(t)$ has the stable density

$$k(x, t) = \frac{t}{\sqrt{2\pi x^3}} e^{-t^2/2x} \qquad (x > 0, t > 0).$$

Then for $t > x > 0$

$$g(t, x) = \frac{1}{\sqrt{2\pi}} \cdot \frac{x}{(t-x)^{3/2}} e^{-t^2/2(t-x)}$$
$$= e^{-2x} \bar{n}(t - x, x),$$

where $\bar{n}(t', x)$ is the inverse Gaussian density

$$\bar{n}(t', x) = \frac{1}{\sqrt{2\pi}} \frac{x}{t'^{3/2}} e^{-(1/2t')(t'-x)^2} \qquad (t' > 0, x > 0).$$

Note that in this case $T(x) < \infty$ with probability e^{-2x}.

EXAMPLE 2 (Example 3 of section 2). Let $X(t)$ have the gamma density

$$k(x, t) = e^{-x/\rho} \rho^{-t} \frac{x^{t-1}}{\Gamma(t)} \qquad (x > 0, t > 0).$$

Then for $t > x > 0$

$$g(t, x) = \frac{x}{t} e^{-(t-x)/\rho} \rho^{-t} \frac{(t-x)^{t-1}}{\Gamma(t)}$$

$$= xe^{-(t-x)/\rho - t \log \rho} t^{t-1} \frac{\left(1 - \frac{x}{t}\right)^{t-1}}{\Gamma(t+1)}.$$

Using the results $\Gamma(t + 1) \sim \sqrt{2\pi} t^{t+(1/2)} e^{-t}$ (Stirling's approximation) and $(1 - (x/t))^{t-1} \sim e^{-x}$ $(t \to \infty)$ we find that

$$g(t, x) \sim \frac{x}{\sqrt{2\pi t^3}} e^{-(t-x)((1/\rho)-1) - t \log \rho} \qquad \text{if } \rho \neq 1,$$

$$\sim \frac{x}{\sqrt{2\pi t^3}} \qquad \text{if } \rho = 1.$$

If $\rho = 1$ we also have

$$P\{T(x) > t\} \sim \sqrt{\frac{2}{\pi}} xt^{-1/2} \qquad (t \to \infty).$$

However, this result is true in the general case $\rho = 1$, $\sigma^2 < \infty$ (see Problem 5).

4.3 The Process $\{T(x), x \geq 0\}$

Returning now to Theorem 5 we note that our proof has revealed the fact that $\{T(x), x \geq 0\}$ is a Lévy process with $Ee^{-sT(x)} = e^{-x\eta(s)}$. We have already seen this in the M/G/1/ system where it was shown that $T(x)$ is a compound Poisson process. From the relation $\eta = s + \phi(\eta)$ we obtain

$$\eta = s + \int_0^\infty (1 - e^{-\eta x})x^{-2}M(dx)$$

$$= s + \int_0^\infty x^{-2}M(dx)\left\{\int_x^\infty (1 - e^{-st})G(dt, x) + (1 - e^{-\eta_0 x})\right\}$$

$$= s + \eta_0 + \int_0^\infty x^{-2}M(dx)\int_x^\infty (1 - e^{-st})G(dt, x),$$

where $G(t, x)$ is the d.f. of $T(x)$ and $\eta_0 \geq 0$. Writing

$$N(dt) = t^2 \int_0^t x^{-2}M(dx)G(dt, x), \qquad (57)$$

we find that

$$\eta = \eta_0 + s + \int_0^\infty (1 - e^{-st})t^{-2}N(dt), \qquad (58)$$

which is of the form (10). The presence of the constant η_0 in (58) indicates the possibility that the event $\{T(x) = \infty\}$ may have a nonzero probability. If $X_0 = \inf\{x: T(x) = \infty\}$ then we define $T(x) = \infty$ for all $x \geq X_0$. Thus the random variable X_0 is the *lifetime* of the process $T(x)$, and $X_0 < \infty$ with probability one iff $\rho > 1$.

In the following theorems we investigate the behavior of $T(x)$ as $x \to \infty$, assuming that the input $X(t)$ has finite mean and variance (see 22). Since $T(x)$ is a Lévy process the limit distribution (if it exists) belongs to the *stable family*. In particular the central limit behavior (Theorem 7 below) is an obvious consequence of the fact that when $\rho < 1$, $T(x)$ has finite mean and variance (Theorem 5). When $\rho = 1$, $T(x)$ has infinite mean and we find the limit distribution to be the stable distribution with exponent $1/2$ (Theorem 8 below).

Theorem 7. *If $\rho < 1$ and $\sigma^2 < \infty$, then*

$$\lim_x P\left\{\frac{T(x) - x(1-\rho)^{-1}}{\sigma\sqrt{x}(1-\rho)^{-3/2}} \leq t\right\} = N(t). \qquad (59)$$

Lemma 3. *If $\rho = 1$ and $\sigma^2 < \infty$, then*

$$\eta(s) = \frac{\sqrt{2s}}{\sigma} + o(s^{1/2}) \qquad (s \to 0+). \qquad (60)$$

PROOF. Under our assumptions $\phi'(0) = \rho = 1$ and $\phi''(0) = -\sigma^2$. Therefore

$$\eta = s + \phi(0) + \eta\phi'(0) + \tfrac{1}{2}\eta^2\phi''(0) + o(\eta^2)$$
$$= s + \eta - \tfrac{1}{2}\sigma^2\eta^2 + o(\eta^2) \qquad (\eta \to 0).$$

This gives

$$\eta^2 = \frac{2s}{\sigma^2} + o(\eta^2) = \frac{2s}{\sigma^2}[1 + o(1)],$$

which leads to the desired result. □

Theorem 8. *If $\rho = 1$ and $\sigma^2 < \infty$, then*

$$\lim_{x \to \infty} P\left\{\frac{\sigma^2 T(x)}{x^2} \le t\right\} = G_{1/2}(t). \tag{61}$$

PROOF. We have

$$Ee^{-s(\sigma^2 T(x)/x^2)} = e^{-x\eta(s\sigma^2/x^2)}.$$

Using Lemma 3 we obtain for each fixed $s > 0$

$$x\eta\left(\frac{s\sigma^2}{x^2}\right) = x\left[\frac{\sqrt{2s}}{x} + o\left(\frac{1}{x}\right)\right] = \sqrt{2s} + o(1) \quad (x \to \infty).$$

Therefore

$$Ee^{-s(\sigma^2 T(x)/x^2)} \to e^{-\sqrt{2s}} \quad (x \to \infty)$$

and the desired result follows since $e^{-\sqrt{2s}}$ is the L.T. of the d.f. $G_{1/2}(t)$. □

5 Insurance Risk: Two Special Cases

We are now in a position to apply the results of sections 3 and 4 to the insurance risk model described in section 1. Here we are concerned with the random variable

$$T(x) = \inf\{t > 0: x + \beta t - X(t) < 0\}, \tag{62}$$

where $x \ge 0$ and $X(t)$ is a compound Poisson process on $(-\infty, \infty)$. The company is interested in evaluating the probability of avoiding ruin over a finite or an infinite horizon, that is,

$$P\{T(x) > t\} \quad (0 < t < \infty) \quad \text{or} \quad P\{T(x) = \infty\}. \tag{63}$$

This is the *ruin problem* of insurance risk theory; we shall call $T(x)$ the *period of prosperity* of the company. We consider below two special cases. The general case will be treated in the next chapter.

(a) *Negative Process.* Let us consider the case of an insurance company that deals only in ordinary whole-life annuities. If we put $\bar{X}(t) = -X(t)$, then the process $\bar{X}(t)$ is seen to be identical (in distribution) with the one considered in the queueing model of section 1. Here $\alpha < 0$, and since β and α are assumed to be of the same sign, $\beta < 0$; without loss of generality we can take $\beta = -1$, so that the risk reserve process becomes $Z(t) = x + \bar{X}(t) - t$, where now $x > 0$. Theorem 5 is immediately applicable, and in particular

$$P\{T(x) = \infty\} = 0 \qquad \text{if } \lambda|\alpha| \leq 1,$$
$$= 1 - e^{-\eta_0 x} \quad \text{if } \lambda|\alpha| > 1.$$

(b) *Positive Process.* We next consider the case where all claims are positive. Here $\alpha > 0$, and as before we take $\beta = 1$. So $Z(t) = x + t - X(t)$ where $x \geq 0$. Writing $Y(t) = X(t) - t$ we note that

$$P\{T(x) > t\} = P\left\{\inf_{0 \leq \tau \leq t} [x - Y(\tau)] \geq 0\right\}$$
$$= P\{M(t) \leq x\}, \tag{64}$$

where M is the supremum functional of Y. Also.

$$P\{T(x) = \infty\} = P\{M(\infty) \leq x\}. \tag{65}$$

In view of (42) the desired results are therefore given by Theorems 2 and 4. Thus the probability (65) is nonzero iff $\lambda\alpha < 1$, and in particular

$$P\{T(0) = \infty\} = 1 - \lambda\alpha \quad \text{if } \lambda\alpha < 1. \tag{66}$$

6 The Ladder Epochs $\{T_k^*\}$

For further analysis of the storage model of section 3 and also to investigate other related models (sections 8 and 9) we need to introduce certain random variables for the next input process $Y(t) = X(t) - t$, where $X(t)$ is the Lévy process defined by (21). Let

$$T_0^* \equiv 0,$$
$$T_k^* = \inf\{t: Y(t) - Y(T_{k-1}^*) > 0\} \qquad (k \geq 1). \tag{67}$$

We call T_k^* the kth (ascending) ladder epoch and $Y(T_k^*)$ the corresponding ladder height. We shall derive the distribution of the kth ladder point $\{T_k^*, Y(T_k^*)\}$. Clearly, the random variables $\{T_k^* - T_{k-1}^*, Y(T_k^*) - Y(T_{k-1}^*), k \geq 1\}$ form a renewal process, so it suffices to consider $\{T_1^*, Y(T_1^*)\}$, where as usual we shall drop the suffixes.

Lemma 4. *For $\theta > 0$, $s > 0$ we have*

$$\int_0^\infty e^{-st} E[e^{\theta Y(t)}; T^* > t] \, dt = \frac{1}{\theta + \eta(s)}. \tag{68}$$

6 The Ladder Epochs $\{T_k^*\}$

PROOF. We have

$$E[e^{\theta Y(t)}; T^* > t] = E[e^{\theta Y(t)}; M(t) = 0]$$
$$= E[e^{-\theta[M(t)-Y(t)]}; M(t) = 0]$$
$$= E[e^{\theta m(t)}; Y(t) - m(t) = 0]$$

by Lemma 1 applied to the Lévy process $Y(t)$. Using Theorem 1 we find that

$$E[e^{\theta m(t)}; Y(t) - m(t) = 0] = E[e^{-\theta I(t)}; Z(t) = 0 | Z(0) = 0]$$

and again, using Theorem 2, we obtain

$$\int_0^\infty e^{-st} E[e^{-\theta I(t)}; Z(t) = 0 | Z(0) = 0] \, dt = J^*(\theta, s) = (\theta + \eta)^{-1}. \quad \square$$

Theorem 9. (i) *For $\theta > 0$, $s > 0$ we have*

$$E[e^{-sT^* - \theta Y(T^*)}] = \frac{\phi(\eta) - \phi(\theta)}{\eta - \theta}. \tag{69}$$

(ii) *The distribution of $\{T^*, Y(T^*)\}$ is proper iff $\rho \geq 1$.*
(iii) *If $\rho > 1$, $E(T^*) = \eta_0^{-1}$ and $EY(T^*) = (\rho - 1)\eta_0^{-1}$. If $\rho = 1$, $E(T^*) = \infty$, $EY(T^*) = \tfrac{1}{2}\sigma^2 \leq \infty$.*

PROOF. We have

$$E[e^{i\omega Y(t)}] = E[e^{i\omega Y(t)}; T^* \leq t] + E[e^{i\omega Y(t)}; T^* > t]. \tag{70}$$

From Lemma 4 we obtain

$$\int_0^\infty e^{-st} E[e^{i\omega Y(t)}; T^* > t] \, dt = (i\omega + \eta)^{-1}. \tag{71}$$

Next we have

$$\int_0^\infty e^{-st} E[e^{i\omega Y(t)}] \, dt = \int_0^\infty e^{-st - i\omega t - t\phi(-i\omega)} \, dt$$
$$= [s + i\omega + \phi(-i\omega)]^{-1} \tag{72}$$

since

$$\text{Re}[s + i\omega + \phi(-i\omega)] = s + \int_0^\infty ((1 - \cos\omega x)x^{-2} M(dx)) > 0.$$

Finally, we have

$$E[e^{i\omega Y(t)}; T^* \leq t] = \int_0^t \int_{0+}^\infty e^{i\omega x} P\{T^* \in d\tau, Y(T^*) \in dx\}$$
$$\cdot E[e^{i\omega[Y(t) - Y(T^*)]} | T^* = \tau, Y(T^*) = x]$$
$$= \int_0^t \int_{0+}^\infty e^{i\omega x} P\{T^* \in d\tau, Y(T^*) \in dx\}$$
$$\cdot E[e^{i\omega Y(t-\tau)}],$$

so that

$$\int_0^\infty e^{-st} E[e^{i\omega Y(t)}; T^* \leq t]\, dt = E[e^{-sT^* + i\omega Y(T^*)}][s + i\omega + \phi(-i\omega)]^{-1}. \quad (73)$$

From (70)–(73) we obtain

$$\frac{1 - E[e^{-sT^* + i\omega Y(T^*)}]}{s + i\omega + \phi(-i\omega)} = \frac{1}{i\omega + \eta}$$

or

$$E[e^{-sT^* + i\omega Y(T^*)}] = \frac{\phi(\eta) - \phi(-i\omega)}{i\omega + \eta},$$

which leads to the desired result (i) expressed in terms of the Laplace transform. Further, we have from (69)

$$P\{T^* < \infty, Y(T^*) < \infty\} = \lim_{s \to 0+} \frac{\phi(\eta)}{\eta}$$

$$= \frac{\phi(\eta_0)}{\eta_0} = 1 \quad \text{if } \rho > 1,$$

$$= \phi'(\eta_0) = \rho \quad \text{if } \rho \leq 1.$$

This proves (ii). From (69) we also have $E(e^{-sT^*}) = \phi(\eta)\eta^{-1} = 1 - s\eta^{-1}$, which can be written as

$$\frac{1 - E(e^{-sT^*})}{s} = \frac{1}{\eta}.$$

For $\rho \geq 1$ this gives

$$E(T^*) = \lim_{s \to 0+} \frac{1 - E(e^{-sT^*})}{s}$$

$$= \eta_0^{-1} \quad \text{if } \rho > 1,$$

$$= \infty \quad \text{if } \rho = 1.$$

Finally, (69) yields the result

$$E[e^{-\theta Y(T^*)}] = \frac{\phi(\theta)}{\theta} \quad \text{if } \rho \leq 1,$$

$$= \frac{\phi(\eta_0) - \phi(\theta)}{\eta_0 - \theta} \quad \text{if } \rho > 1.$$

Form this $EY(T^*)$ is obtained in the usual manner by differentiation. This completes the proof. □

Theorem 10. Let $N(t) = \max\{k: T_k^* \leq t\}$. If $\rho = 1$, $\sigma^2 < \infty$, then

$$\lim_{t \to \infty} P\left\{\frac{\sigma N(t)}{2\sqrt{t}} < x\right\} = N_+(x). \quad (74)$$

PROOF. From (69) we obtain $E(e^{sT^*}) = 1 - s\eta^{-1}$. Using Lemma 3 we find that

$$1 - E(e^{-sT^*}) = \frac{\sigma}{\sqrt{2}} s^{1/2} + o(s^{1/2}) \qquad (s \to 0+).$$

Therefore

$$E(e^{-(4s/\sigma^2)T_k^*/k^2}) = \left[1 - \frac{\sqrt{2s}}{k} + o\left(\frac{1}{k}\right)\right]^k \to e^{-\sqrt{2s}}$$

as $k \to \infty$. Since $e^{-\sqrt{2s}}$ is the L.T. of the stable d.f. $G_{1/2}(x)$ it follows that as $k \to \infty$

$$P\left\{\frac{4T_k^*}{\sigma^2 k^2} \leq x\right\} \to G_{1/2}(x). \tag{75}$$

Now we have

$$P\{N(t) < k\} = P\{T_k^* > t\},$$

which can be written as

$$P\left\{\frac{\sigma N(t)}{2\sqrt{t}} < \frac{k\sigma}{2\sqrt{t}}\right\} = P\left\{\frac{4T_k^*}{\sigma^2 k^2} > \frac{4t}{\sigma^2 k^2}\right\}. \tag{76}$$

In this let $k \to \infty$, $t \to \infty$ in such a way that $k\sigma/2\sqrt{t} \to x > 0$ (fixed). Then by (75) the right side of (76) converges to

$$1 - G_{1/2}(x^{-2}) = 2N(x) - 1 = N_+(x)$$

and therefore

$$P\left\{\frac{\sigma N(t)}{2\sqrt{t}} < x\right\} \to N_+(x)$$

as required. □

7 Limit Theorems for the Storage Model

In this section we derive limit theorems for the processes $Z(t)$ and $I(t)$ in the storage model of section 3.

Theorem 11. (i) If $1 < \rho < \infty$ and $\sigma^2 < \infty$, then

$$\lim_{t \to \infty} P\left\{\frac{Z(t) - (\rho - 1)t}{\sigma\sqrt{t}} \leq x\right\} = N(x). \tag{77}$$

(ii) If $\rho < 1$ and $\sigma^2 < \infty$, then

$$\lim_{t \to \infty} P\left\{\frac{I(t) - (1 - \rho)t}{\sigma\sqrt{t}} \leq x\right\} = N(x). \tag{78}$$

PROOF. We have $Z(t) = Z(0) + Y(t) + I(t)$, so that

$$\frac{Z(t)-(\rho-1)t}{\sigma\sqrt{t}} = \frac{Z(0)}{\sigma\sqrt{t}} + \frac{Y(t)-(\rho-1)t}{\sigma\sqrt{t}} + \frac{I(t)}{\sigma\sqrt{t}}. \tag{79}$$

Clearly, $Z(0)/\sqrt{t} \to 0$ as $t \to \infty$. Also, when $\rho > 1$, $I(t)$ has a limit distribution by Theorem 3, so $I(t)/\sqrt{t} \to 0$ in distribution. Therefore the limit distribution of the random variable on the left side of (79) is the same as that of the second term on the right side, and this latter is the normal distribution, since the net input $Y(t)$ is a Lévy process with mean $(\rho-1)t$ and variance $\sigma^2 t$. This proves (i), and the proof of (ii) is similar. □

Theorem 12. *If $\rho = 1$ and $\sigma^2 < \infty$, then*

$$\lim_{t\to\infty} P\left\{\frac{I(t)}{\sigma\sqrt{t}} < x\right\} = N_+(x), \tag{80}$$

and

$$\lim_{t\to\infty} P\left\{\frac{Z(t)}{\sigma\sqrt{t}} \le x\right\} = N_+(x). \tag{81}$$

PROOF. Without loss of generality we assume $Z(0) \equiv 0$. Then from (32) and (42) we have $I(t) = -m(t)$ and $Z(t) \sim M(t)$. Therefore

$$P\{I(t) < x\} = P\{m(t) > -x\} = P\{T(x) > t\} \tag{82}$$

and

$$P\left\{\frac{I(t)}{\sigma\sqrt{t}} < x\right\} = P\{T(\sigma x\sqrt{t}) > t\} = P\left\{\sigma^2 \frac{T(\sigma x\sqrt{t})}{\sigma^2 x^2 t} > \frac{1}{x^2}\right\}$$

$$\to 1 - G_{1/2}\left(\frac{1}{x^2}\right) = N_+(x)$$

by Theorem 8. This proves (80). For (81) it suffices to consider $M(t)$. We have

$$M(t) = M_1 + M_2 + \cdots + M_{N(t)},$$

where $M_k = Y(T_k^*) - Y(T_{k-1}^*)$ $(k \ge 1)$ and $N(t) = \max\{k: T_k^* \le t\}$, and T_k^* are the ladder epochs defined in section 6. Therefore

$$\frac{M(t)}{\sigma\sqrt{t}} = \frac{M_1 + M_2 + \cdots + M_{N(t)}}{E(M_1)N(t)} \cdot \frac{\sigma N(t)}{2\sqrt{t}} \tag{83}$$

since $E(M_1) = \tfrac{1}{2}\sigma^2$ by Theorem 9. The first factor on the right side of (83) tends to unity as $t \to \infty$ by the strong law of large numbers, while the second factor converges in distribution by Theorem 10. The result (81) follows immediately. □

Remark. The storage process $\{Z(t), t \geq 0\}$ described in section 3 is a Markov process, although our analysis of it does not directly depend on its Markov properties. The transition d.f. of $Z(t)$ is given by

$$F(x; y, t) = P\{Z(t) \leq y \mid Z(0) = x\}$$
$$= P\{Y(t) \leq y - x, Y(t) - m(t) \leq y\}$$

using Theorem 1. Proceeding as in the proof of Lemma 1 we find that $\{M(t), Y(t)\} \sim \{Y(t) - m(t), Y(t)\}$, so that we can write in particular,

$$F(x; 0, t) = P\{Y(t) \leq -x, M(t) = 0\}$$
$$= P\{Y(t) \leq -x, T^* > t\}. \tag{84}$$

Lemma 4 is therefore essentially a statement concerning $F(x; 0, t)$. We recall from (40) that

$$F^*(x; 0, s) = \int_0^\infty e^{-st} F(x; 0, t) \, dt = \frac{e^{-x\eta}}{\eta}. \tag{85}$$

If $\rho \geq 1$ we know from Theorem 4 that $F(x; 0, t) \to 0$ as $t \to \infty$. Theorem 13 below describes the behavior of $F(x; 0, t)$ for large t in the case $\rho = 1$, $\sigma^2 < \infty$.

Theorem 13. *If $\rho = 1$ and $\sigma^2 < \infty$, then for $x \geq 0$ we have*

$$F(x; 0, t) = \frac{\sigma}{\sqrt{2\pi}} t^{-1/2} + o(t^{-1/2}) \qquad (t \to \infty). \tag{86}$$

PROOF. From (85) and Lemma 3 we find that

$$F^*(0; 0, s) = \frac{\sigma}{\sqrt{2}} s^{-1/2} + o(s^{-1/2}) \qquad (s \to 0+).$$

Also, we have from (84)

$$F(0; 0, t) = P\{T^* > t\}$$

which shows that $F(0; 0, t)$ is a monotone (nonincreasing) function. Therefore by a Tauberian theorem it follows that

$$F(0; 0, t) \sim \frac{\sigma}{\sqrt{2\pi}} t^{-1/2} \qquad (t \to \infty). \tag{87}$$

We have thus proved (86) for $x = 0$. For $x > 0$, using the strong Markov property of $Y(t)$ we obtain

$$F(x; 0, t) = \int_0^t G(d\tau, x) F(0; 0, t - \tau)$$
$$= \int_0^1 G(t \, du, x) F(0; 0, t - tu),$$

so that

$$t^{1/2}F(x; 0, t) = \int_0^1 G(t\, du, x)[t(1-u)]^{1/2} F(0; 0, t-tu)(1-u)^{-1/2}.$$

Using (87) and the fact that with probability one $T(x)/t \to 0$ as $t \to \infty$ we therefore obtain

$$t_{1/2} F(x; 0, t) \to \frac{\sigma}{\sqrt{2\pi}} \int_0^1 E_0(du)(1-u)^{-1/2},$$

where $E_0(x) = 0$ for $x < 0$ and $= 1$ for $x \geq 0$. The integral reduces to unity and we have thus proved (86) for $x > 0$, as required. □

8 A Second Storage Model

The model described in section 3 is that of a store with infinite capacity, which has the policy of meeting demands as long as physically possible. If the capacity is finite, say c ($0 < c < \infty$), then there arises the possibility of a part of the input being lost on account of overflow. It is not known whether there exists any simple modification of the integral equation (19) that will represent the storage process $Z(t)$ in this case, or indeed any expression for $Z(t)$ in terms of the basic process $Y(t)$ and its supremum or infimum functionals.

Let us, however, consider a third model, namely that of a dam of infinite depth, whose level $\bar{Z}(t)$ is measured from an arbitrary origin. Thus the process $\bar{Z}(t)$ has the state space $(-\infty, c]$. Overflows are assumed to occur instantaneously, so that at the epochs they occur, $Z(t) = c$. The net input process $Y(t)$ is the same as in section 3, namely $Y(t) = X(t) - t$, where $X(t)$ is a Lévy process defined by (21). To be more precise, we define a sequence of random variables $\{T_k^*, k \geq 1\}$ as follows. Let $x \leq c$, and

$$T_1^* = \inf\{t: Y(t) > c - x\},$$
$$T_k^* = \inf\{t: Y(t) - Y(T_{k-1}^*) > 0\} \quad (k \geq 2). \tag{88}$$

We define the storage process $\{\bar{Z}(t), t \geq 0\}$ as follows:

$$\bar{Z}(t) = x + Y(t) \quad \text{for } 0 \leq t < T_1^*$$
$$= c + Y(t) - Y(T_k^*) \quad \text{for } T_k^* \leq t < T_{k+1}^* \quad (k \geq 1). \tag{89}$$

The random variables T_k^* ($k \geq 2$) have the same distribution as the ladder epochs defined in section 6, while T_1^* has the same distribution as the first ladder epoch iff $x = c$. However, T_1^*, $T_k^* - T_{k-1}^*$ ($k \geq 2$) are mutually independent, and consequently $T_k^* \to \infty$ as $k \to \infty$ with probability one. Therefore the process $\bar{Z}(t)$ is well defined.

The overflows occur at the epochs T_k^* and the amounts of successive overflows are $\bar{I}_k$ ($k \geq 1$), where

$$\bar{I}_1 = x + Y(T_1^*) - c$$
$$\bar{I}_k = Y(T_k^*) - Y(T_{k-1}^*) \quad (k \geq 2). \tag{90}$$

The total overflow up to time t is given by $\bar{I}(t)$, where

$$\bar{I}(t) = 0 \qquad \text{for } 0 \leq t < T_1^*$$
$$= x - c + Y(T_k^*) \quad \text{for } T_k^* \leq t < T_{k+1}^* \quad (k \geq 1). \tag{91}$$

The following theorem expresses $\bar{Z}(t)$, $\bar{I}(t)$ in terms of $M(t)$, $m(t)$, the supremum and infimum functionals of $Y(t)$.

Theorem 14. (i) *If* $\bar{Z}(0) = x \leq c$, *we have*

$$\bar{Z}(t) = \min\{x + Y(t), c + Y(t) - M(t)\}, \tag{92}$$
$$\bar{I}(t) = \max\{0, x - c + M(t)\}. \tag{93}$$

(ii) *If* $\bar{Z}(0) = c$, *then*

$$\bar{Z}(t) \sim c - I(t), \qquad \bar{I}(t) \sim Z(t), \tag{94}$$

where $Z(t), I(t)$ *refer to the model of section 3, with* $Z(0) = 0$.

PROOF. Since $\bar{Z}(t) + \bar{I}(t) = x + Y(t)$, as is evident from (89) and (91), it suffices to prove (93), We have

$$M(t) \leq c - x \quad \text{for } 0 \leq t < T_1^*$$
$$= Y(T_k^*) \quad \text{for } T_k^* \leq t < T_{k+1}^* \quad (k \geq 1). \tag{95}$$

The equations (91) therefore lead to (93). If $x = c$, then (92)–(93) reduce to

$$\bar{Z}(t) = c + Y(t) - M(t), \qquad \bar{I}(t) = M(t). \tag{96}$$

Lemma 1 applied to the process $Y(t)$ then yields (94). $\square$

Theorem 15. (i) *For* $x \leq c, z \leq c, y \geq 0$ *we have*

$$P\{\bar{Z}(t) < z, \bar{I}(t) \leq y \mid \bar{Z}(0) = x\}$$
$$= P\{Z(t) < c - x, I(t) = 0 \mid Z(0) = c - z\} \tag{97}$$
$$+ P\{Z(t) \leq c + y - x, I(t) > c - z \mid Z(0) = 0\}.$$

(ii) *For* $x = c, z \leq c, y \geq 0$ *we have*

$$P\{\bar{Z}(t) < z, \bar{I}(t) \leq y \mid \bar{Z}(0) = c\} = P\{Z(t) \leq y, I(t) > c - z \mid Z(0) = 0\}. \tag{98}$$

PROOF. Using Theorem 14 we find that

$$P\{\bar{Z}(t) < z, \bar{I}(t) \leq y | \bar{Z}(0) = x\}$$
$$= P\{\min[x + Y(t), c + m(t)] < z, \max[0, x - c + Y(t) - m(t)] \leq y\}$$
$$= P\{x - c + Y(t) - m(t) < 0, x + Y(t) < z\}$$
$$+ P\{0 \leq x - c + Y(t) - m(t) \leq y, c + m(t) < z\}$$
$$= P\{Y(t) - m(t) < c - x, Y(t) < z - x\}$$
$$+ P\{Y(t) - m(t) \leq c + y - x, m(t) < z - c\}$$
$$- P\{Y(t) - m(t) < c - x, Y(t) < z - x, m(t) < z - c\},$$

since $Y(t) - m(t) < c - x$, $m(t) < z - c$ imply $Y(t) < z - x$. On account of Theorem 1 the left side of (97) therefore equals

$$P\{Z(t) < c - x | Z(0) = c - z\}$$
$$+ P\{Z(t) \leq c + y - x, I(t) > c - z | Z(0) = 0\}$$
$$- P\{Z(t) < c - x, I(t) > 0 | Z(0) = c - z\},$$

which reduces to the right side of (97). The result (98) follows from (97). □

Theorems 14 and 15 reveal the *duality relationship* between the process $\{\bar{Z}(t), \bar{I}(t)\}$ arising from the present model and the process $\{Z(t), I(t)\}$ of section 3. The limit behavior of $\bar{Z}(t)$ and $\bar{I}(t)$ is an easy consequence of this duality, as described below in Theorems 16 and 17. For further results see Problem 15.

Theorem 16. *We have*

$$P\{\bar{I}(t) \leq y | \bar{Z}(0) = x\} = P\{Z(t) \leq c + y - x | Z(0) = 0\} \quad (99)$$

and

$$\lim_{t \to \infty} P\{\bar{I}(t) \leq y | \bar{Z}(0) = x\} = 0 \quad \text{if } \rho \geq 1$$
$$= F(c + y - x) \quad \text{if } \rho < 1, \quad (100)$$

where $F(x)$ is the limit d.f. of $Z(t)$.

PROOF. Letting $z \to c+$ in (97) we obtain

$$P\{\bar{I}(t) \leq y | \bar{Z}(0) = x\} = P\{Z(t) < c - x, I(t) = 0 | Z(0) = 0\}$$
$$+ P\{Z(t) \leq c + y - x, I(t) > 0 | Z(0) = 0\}$$

and this leads to (99) since by Corollary 1 we have $I(t) > 0$ with probability one if $Z(0) = 0$. The result (100) is obvious. □

Theorem 17. *We have*

$$P\{\bar{Z}(t) < z | \bar{Z}(0) = x\} = P\{Z(t) < c - x, I(t) = 0 | Z(0) = c - z\}$$
$$+ P\{I(t) > c - z | Z(0) = 0\} \quad (101)$$

and

$$\lim_{t \to \infty} P\{\bar{Z}(t) < z | \bar{Z}(0) = x\} = 1 \quad \text{if } \rho \leq 1,$$
$$= e^{\eta_0(z-c)} \quad \text{if } \rho > 1. \quad (102)$$

PROOF. The result (101) follows from (97) by letting $y \to \infty$. To prove (102) we note that

$$P\{Z(t) < c - x, I(t) = 0 | Z(0) = c - z\} \leq P\{I(t) = 0 | Z(0) = c - z\} \to 0$$

if $\rho \leq 1$, since in this case $I(t) \to \infty$ with probability one by Theorem 3. Also,

$$P\{Z(t) < c - x, I(t) = 0 | Z(0) = c - z\} \leq P\{Z(t) < c - x | Z(0) = c - z\} \to 0$$

if $\rho > 1$, since $Z(t) \to \infty$ in distribution by Theorem 4. Thus the first term on the right side of (101) converges to zero for all ρ, and the second term converges to the required limit by Theorem 3. □

9 The Queue G/M/1

The waiting time in a queueing system is defined as the time a customer would have to wait for the commencement of his service. From the point of view of a potential customer, this definition serves as an adequate description of the system, and leads to useful results in particular cases such as M/G/1 and related systems (see sections 10 and 11). However, in practice, this waiting time process cannot be observed, since it is defined in terms of random variables whose values are not known at time t, namely, service times of customers present at time t but not yet served. For this reason we propose to define the waiting time as the time the customer at the counter has already spent in the system. Denoting this waiting time as $\bar{W}(t)$, we formulate our definition as follows: If at time t the counter is unoccupied, we put $\bar{W}(t) = 0$; otherwise $\bar{W}(t)$ is the time that has elapsed since the arrival of the customer being served at time t. If at time t, $\bar{W}(t) > 0$, it increases continuously at a unit rate as long as the customer at the counter continues to be served, but when his service is completed, $\bar{W}(t)$ decreases by an amount u, where u is the interval of time between his arrival and that of the customer who had followed him. Thus if $\{t_n, n \geq 1\}$ are the successive epochs of departure from the system, we have

$$\bar{W}(t) = \max\{0, \bar{W}(t_n-) - u_n + t - t_n\}, \quad t_n \leq t < t_{n+1}, \quad (n \geq 1), \quad (103)$$

where u_n is the interval of time between the $(n-1)$st and nth arrivals. Thus the process $\{\bar{W}(t),\ t \geq 0\}$ has discontinuities at the points t_n; we define $\bar{W}(t_n) = \bar{W}(t_n+)$, so that the process is right-continuous.

We shall investigate the process $\bar{W}(t)$ defined above in the special case of the single-server queueing system G/M/1, where the inter-arrival times $\{u_k,\ k \geq 1\}$ of customers are independent random variables with a common d.f. $B(x)$, and the service times have density $\lambda e^{-\lambda x}$ $(0 < \lambda < \infty)$. From (103) it is clear that the basic process of this system is given by $\bar{Y}(t) = t - X(t)$, where

$$X(t) = u_1 + u_2 + \cdots + u_{D(t)}, \qquad (104)$$

$D(t)$ being the maximum number of customers that can be served during a time interval $(0, t]$ if a sufficient number were present. Clearly, $D(t)$ is a simple Poisson process with parameter λ, and $X(t)$ is therefore a compound Poisson process with

$$Ee^{-\theta X(t)} = e^{-\lambda t[1 - \psi(\theta)]}, \qquad (105)$$

where $\psi(\theta)$ is the L.T. of the d.f. $B(x)$. We shall denote $\phi(\theta) = \lambda - \lambda\psi(\theta)$. We have

$$EX(t) = \frac{t}{\bar{\rho}}, \qquad \operatorname{Var} X(t) = \sigma^2 t, \qquad (106)$$

where $\bar{\rho} = [\lambda E(u_1)]^{-1} \leq \infty$, and $\sigma^2 = \lambda E(u_1^2) \leq \infty$. For the net input process $\bar{Y}(t)$ we have $\bar{Y}(t) = -Y(t)$, where $Y(t)$ is as defined in section 3, and we shall therefore use most of the notation used there. In particular, $\eta \equiv \eta(s)$ is the root of the functional equation $\eta = s + \phi(\eta)$. Note that $\bar{\rho}$ is the traffic intensity of the system, and $\bar{\rho} = \rho^{-1}$.

Our analysis of the process $\bar{W}(t)$ is based on its *regenerative property*. Specifically, let us assume that the system starts at time $t = 0$ with just one customer, who is commencing his service, and denote the successive busy cycles as $\bar{Z}_1, \bar{Z}_2, \ldots$. Then at every epoch $\bar{Z}_1 + \bar{Z}_2 + \cdots + \bar{Z}_k$ $(k \geq 1)$ the process $\bar{W}(t)$ starts from scratch, that is, given $\bar{Z}_1 + \bar{Z}_2 + \cdots + \bar{Z}_k = \tau$, the distribution of $\bar{W}(t)$ is the same as that of $\bar{W}(t - \tau)$ and independent of $\bar{Z}_1 + \bar{Z}_2 + \cdots + \bar{Z}_k$. Here $\bar{Z}_k = \bar{T}_k + \bar{I}_k$, where $\bar{T}_k$ is the kth busy period and $\bar{I}_k$ the idle period that follows this busy period $(k \geq 1)$. the $\bar{Z}_k$ are mutually independent random variables with a common d.f., and therefore it suffices to consider $\bar{Z}_1 = \bar{T}_1 + \bar{I}_1$, where we shall as usual drop the suffixes. From (103) we see that

$$\bar{T} = \inf\{t\colon \bar{Y}(t) < 0\}, \qquad \bar{I} = -\bar{Y}(\bar{T}). \qquad (107)$$

We have then the following.

Theorem 18. *For the queueing system G/M/1 we have the following.*

(i) *The L.T. of the distribution of $(\bar{T}, \bar{I})$ is given by*

$$E(e^{-s\bar{T} - \theta \bar{I}}) = \frac{\phi(\eta) - \phi(\theta)}{\eta - \theta} \qquad (s > 0,\ \theta > 0). \qquad (108)$$

9 The Queue G/M/1

(ii) *For the busy cycle $\bar{Z} = \bar{T} + \bar{I}$ we have*

$$E(e^{-s\bar{Z}}) = 1 - \frac{\phi(s)}{\phi(\eta)}. \tag{109}$$

(iii) *The distribution of $\bar{Z}$ is proper iff $\bar{\rho} \leq 1$, in which case*

$$\begin{aligned} E(\bar{Z}) &= (\bar{\rho}\eta_0)^{-1} \quad \text{if } \bar{\rho} < 1, \\ &= \infty \quad \text{if } \bar{\rho} = 1. \end{aligned} \tag{110}$$

(iv) *Let $\bar{U}(t) = 1 +$ expected number of busy cycles in $(0, t]$. Then $\bar{U}(\infty) = \infty$ if $\bar{\rho} \leq 1$, and $\bar{U}(\infty) = (1 - \rho)^{-1}$ if $\bar{\rho} > 1$. Also, if $\bar{\rho} = 1$ and $\sigma^2 < \infty$, then*

$$\bar{U}(t) \sim \frac{2^{3/2}}{\sigma\sqrt{\pi}} t^{1/2} \quad (t \to \infty). \tag{111}$$

PROOF. The random variable $\bar{T}$ has the same distribution as the first ladder epoch of the process $Y(t)$, defined in section 6. The results (i)–(iii) therefore follow from Theorem 9. To prove (iv) we note that

$$\bar{U}(t) = \sum_{k=0}^{\infty} P\{\bar{Z}_1 + \bar{Z}_2 + \cdots + \bar{Z}_k \leq t\},$$

so that

$$\bar{U}^*(s) = \int_0^{\infty} e^{-st} \bar{U}(dt) = (1 - Ee^{-s\bar{Z}_1})^{-1}$$

and using (109),

$$\bar{U}^*(s) = \frac{\phi(\eta)}{\phi(s)} \quad (s > 0).$$

Therefore

$$\begin{aligned} \bar{U}(\infty) &= \lim_{s \to 0+} U^*(s) \\ &= \infty \quad \text{if } \rho > 1, \\ &= (1 - \rho)^{-1} \quad \text{if } \rho \leq 1. \end{aligned}$$

In this case $\bar{\rho} = 1$, $\sigma^2 < \infty$ we use Lemma 3 and find that

$$\bar{U}^*(s) = \frac{\eta - s}{\phi(s)} = \frac{\frac{\sqrt{2}}{\sigma} s^{1/2} + o(s^{1/2})}{s + o(s)}$$

$$= \frac{\sqrt{2}}{\sigma} s^{-1/2} + o(s^{-1/2}) \quad (s \to 0+).$$

A Tauberian theorem then yields (111), and the theorem is completely proved. □

Theorem 19. *For the process $\bar{W}(t)$ in the system G/M/1 we have the following*:

$$P\{\bar{W}(t) \geq x\} = \int_{0-}^{t} \bar{U}(d\tau) F(x; 0, t - \tau) \qquad (x > 0, t > 0) \qquad (112)$$

and

$$\lim_{t \to \infty} P\{\bar{W}(t) \geq x\} = 1 \qquad \text{if } \bar{\rho} \geq 1$$
$$= \bar{\rho} e^{-\eta_0 x} \qquad \text{if } \bar{\rho} < 1. \qquad (113)$$

PROOF. We have

$$P\{\bar{W}(t) \geq x\} = P\{\bar{W}(t) \geq x, \bar{Z}_1 > t\} + \int_0^t P\{\bar{Z}_1 \in d\tau\} P\{\bar{W}(t) \geq x | \bar{Z}_1 = \tau\}.$$

The regenerative property described above gives

$$P\{\bar{W}(t) \geq x | \bar{Z}_1 = \tau\} = P\{\bar{W}(t - \tau) \geq x\}.$$

Also,

$$P\{\bar{W}(t) \geq x, \bar{Z}_1 > t\} = P\{\bar{W}(t) \geq x, \bar{T}_1 > t\} = P\{\bar{Y}(t) \geq x, \bar{T}_1 > t\}$$
$$= P\{Y(t) \leq -x, T_1^* > t\},$$

and this last probability equals $F(x; 0, t)$ on account of (84). Thus writing $\bar{F}(x, t) = P\{\bar{W}(t) \geq x\}$ we see that $\bar{F}(x, t)$ satisfies the integral equation

$$\bar{F}(x, t) = F(x; 0, t) + \int_0^t P\{\bar{Z}_1 \in d\tau\} \bar{F}(x, t - \tau), \qquad (114)$$

which is the integral equation of renewal theory. It is known that (114) has the unique solution given by (12).

From (84) we see that $F(x; 0, t) \leq F(0; 0, t)$, where $F(0; 0, t)$ is a monotone (nonincreasing) function. Therefore $F(x; 0, t)$ is directly Riemann integrable over $(0 < t < \infty)$, and in the case $\bar{\rho} < 1$ we find that

$$\infty \geq \int_0^\infty F(x; 0, t) \, dt = \lim_{s \to 0+} \int_0^\infty e^{-st} F(x; 0, t) \, dt$$
$$= \lim_{s \to 0+} \frac{e^{-x\eta}}{\eta} = \frac{e^{-x\eta_0}}{\eta_0}.$$

Also, in this case $E(\bar{Z}_1) = (\bar{\rho}\eta_0)^{-1}$ from (110). The renewal theorem then gives

$$\lim_{t \to \infty} \bar{F}(x, t) = \frac{1}{E(\bar{Z}_1)} \int_0^\infty F(x; 0, t) \, dt = \bar{\rho} e^{-x\eta_0}$$

as required for $\bar{\rho} < 1$.

If $\bar{\rho} > 1$, then (112) gives

$$\lim_{t \to \infty} \bar{F}(x, t) = \bar{U}(\infty) \lim_{t \to \infty} F(x; 0, t) = (1 - \rho)^{-1}(1 - \rho) = 1.$$

Finally, if $\bar{\rho} = 1$, $\sigma^2 < \infty$ we use (111) and (86) in (112) and find that

$$\bar{F}(x, t) = \int_0^1 \bar{U}(t\,ds) F(x; 0, t - ts)$$

$$= \int_0^1 \frac{\bar{U}(t\,ds)}{\bar{U}(t)} (t - ts)^{1/2} F(x; 0, t - ts) t^{-1/2} \bar{U}(t)(1 - s)^{-1/2}$$

$$\to \int_0^1 \frac{1}{2} s^{-1/2}\, ds \frac{\sigma}{\sqrt{2\pi}} \frac{2^{3/2}}{\sigma\sqrt{\pi}} (1 - s)^{-1/2}$$

$$= \frac{1}{\pi} \int_0^1 s^{-1/2} (1 - s)^{-1/2}\, ds = 1,$$

as required. The proof is thus complete. □

10 Queues with Static Priorities

We consider a single-server queueing system in which the customers belong to two classes (numbered 0 and 1). They arrive in two independent Poisson processes at rates λ_0 and λ_1, and their service times have d.f.'s $B_0(x)$ and $B_1(x)$ respectively. Let

$$\rho_i = \lambda_i \int_0^\infty x\, dB_i(x), \qquad \sigma_i^2 = \lambda_i \int_0^\infty x^2\, dB_i(x), \qquad (115)$$

where $0 < \rho_i \le \infty$, $0 < \sigma_i^2 \le \infty$, $(i = 0, 1)$. The queue discipline is based on *static priorities*, namely, class 0 customers receive low priority for service, while class 1 customers receive high priority, these priorities being determined before the customers' arrival. We consider here the case where the priority is of the *pre-emptive resume* or *head-of-the-line* type.

We are interested in the virtual waiting times of low and high priority customers. Under the pre-emptive discipline the virtual waiting time $W_1(t)$ of a high priority customer is unaffected by the presence of low priority customers, and the results of section 3 apply to it. However, under the head-of-the-line discipline $W_1(t)$ is not amenable to any easy treatment. We shall therefore be concerned with $W_0(t)$, the virtual waiting time of a low priority customer. It turns out that the distribution of $W_0(t)$ can be obtained directly from the results of sections 3 and 4. This can be seen as follows. Let us denote by $X_i(t)$ the workload that is submitted to the server in a time interval $(0, t]$ by customers of class i; then as in section 1, we see that $X_i(t)$ is a compound Poisson process $(i = 0, 1)$. Our assumptions imply that $X_0(t)$ and $X_1(t)$ are independent, and therefore their sum,

$$X(t) = X_0(t) + X_1(t), \qquad (116)$$

is again a compound Poisson process with the d.f.

$$P\{X(t) \le x\} = \sum_{n=0}^{\infty} e^{-\lambda t} \frac{(\lambda t)^n}{n!} B_n(x), \tag{117}$$

where

$$\lambda = \lambda_0 + \lambda_1, \qquad \lambda B(x) = \lambda_0 B_0(x) + \lambda_1 B_1(x). \tag{118}$$

We have $EX(t) = \rho t$ and $\operatorname{Var} X(t) = \sigma^2 t$, where

$$\rho = \lambda \int_0^{\infty} x \, dB(x) = \rho_0 + \rho_1, \qquad \sigma^2 = \lambda \int_0^{\infty} x^2 \, dB(x) = \sigma_0^2 + \sigma_1^2. \tag{119}$$

Also, the L.T. of $B(x)$ is given by $\psi(\theta)$, where

$$\lambda \psi(\theta) = \lambda_0 \psi_0(\theta) + \lambda_1 \psi_1(\theta) \qquad (\theta > 0), \tag{120}$$

$\psi_0(\theta)$, $\psi_1(\theta)$ being the L.T.'s of $B_0(x)$, $B_1(x)$ respectively. We have $Ee^{-\theta X(t)} = e^{-t\phi(\theta)}$, where $\phi(\theta) = \lambda - \lambda \psi(\theta)$. Let us denote by $\eta \equiv \eta(s)$ the unique continuous solution of the functional equation

$$\eta = s + \lambda - \lambda \psi(\eta) \qquad (s > 0), \tag{121}$$

with $\eta(\infty) = \infty$. We have then the following result.

Theorem 20. *Let $W(t)$ be the remaining workload of the server at time t, regardless of the priorities associated with the customers. Then*

$$\int_0^{\infty} e^{-st} E[e^{-\theta W(t)} \,|\, W(0) = 0] = \frac{1 - \theta/\eta}{s - \theta + \lambda - \lambda \psi(\theta)} \qquad (\theta > 0, \, s > 0), \tag{122}$$

where η is given by (121).

PROOF. It is clear that $W(t)$ is the sum of the residual service time of the customer at the counter (of low or high priority) and the service times of all other customers present at time t. The arrival of each customer increases this load, while the server continuously exhausts this load at a unit rate except when the system is empty. This statement is true under the pre-emptive resume or head-of-the-line discipline that we have assumed, but is false under pre-emptive repeat discipline, where the time spent on a low priority customer is wasted when he is displaced by a high priority customer. Therefore $W(t)$ satisfies the integral equation

$$W(t) = W(0) + X(t) - t + \int_0^t \chi(s) \, ds, \tag{123}$$

where $\chi(t) = 1$ if $W(t) = 0$ and $= 0$ otherwise. This equation is identical with (19) and so the desired result follows from Corollary 1. □

For convenience we shall assume that $W(0) = 0$ from now on. To complete the formulation of $W_0(t)$ we now define for each fixed $t \geq 0$, the process $\{W_t(t'), t' \geq 0\}$ as follows:

$$W_t(t') = W_t(0) + X_1(t + t') - X_1(t) - t' + \int_0^{t'} \chi_t(s)\, ds, \quad (124)$$

where $\chi_t(t') = 1$ if $W_t(t') = 0$ and $= 0$ otherwise. Clearly, $W_t(t')$ represents the workload arising from all class 1 arrivals during the time interval $(t, t + t']$, starting with an initial workload $W_t(0)$. The integral equation (124) is similar to the basic equation (19), and therefore yields a unique solution. We also define the random variable

$$T_t = \inf\{t': W_t(t') = 0\}, \quad (125)$$

which is the duration of the busy period in terms of class 1 customers. If $W_t(0) = w \geq 0$, we shall denote T_t as $T_t(w)$. We have now the following.

Theorem 21. *The low priority customer's virtual waiting time $W_0(t)$ is given by*

$$W_0(t) = T_t[W(t)]. \quad (126)$$

For the L.T. of $W_0(t)$ we have

$$\int_0^\infty e^{-st} E[e^{-\theta W_0(t)}]\, dt = \frac{1 - \eta_1/\eta}{s - \eta_1 + \lambda - \lambda \psi(\eta_1)} \quad (\theta > 0, s > 0), \quad (127)$$

where $\eta_1 \equiv \eta_1(\theta)$ is the unique continuous solution of the equation

$$\eta_1 = \theta + \lambda_1 - \lambda_1 \psi_1(\eta_1), \quad (128)$$

with $\eta_1(\infty) = \infty$, and $\eta \equiv \eta(s)$ is given by (121). Furthermore,

$$\lim_{t \to \infty} E[e^{-\theta W_0(t)}] = \frac{(1 - \rho_0 - \rho_1)\eta_1(\theta)}{\eta_1 - \lambda + \lambda \psi(\eta_1)} \quad \text{if } \rho_0 + \rho_1 < 1,$$

$$= 0 \quad \text{if } \rho_0 + \rho_1 \geq 1. \quad (129)$$

PROOF. Under static priorities a class 0 customer arriving at time t has to wait for all class 0 and class 1 customers present at that time to complete their service (the total time required for this being $W(t)$ by definition), and also for all subsequent class 1 customers. Therefore the waiting time of this customer is given by (126), where $W_0(0) = T_t(0) = 0$, as we have assumed $W(0) = 0$. Now we recall from Theorem 5 that $Ee^{-\theta T_1(w)} = e^{-w\eta_1}$ where η_1 is given by (128). From (122) and (126) we therefore obtain

$$\int_0^\infty e^{-st} E[e^{-\theta W_0(t)}]\, dt = \int_0^\infty e^{-st} E[e^{-\eta_1 W(t)}]\, dt$$

$$= \frac{1 - \eta_1/\eta}{s - \eta_1 + \lambda - \lambda \psi(\eta_1)},$$

as required. The limit result (129) follows from (127) in the usual manner, and the proof is complete. □

The situations where
$$\rho_0 + \rho_1 = 1 \tag{130a}$$
or
$$\rho_0 + \rho_1 > 1, \qquad \rho_1 \le 1 \tag{130b}$$
are also of interest. In these cases it will be found that limit distributions exist for $W_0(t)$ when it is reduced with a proper choice of location and scale parameters (necessarily depending on t). Again our results follow from those of sections 4 and 7 concerning the limit distributions of $W(t)$ as $t \to \infty$ and of $T_1(x)$ as $x \to \infty$. The only novel feature appears in the case $\rho_1 = 1$, where the scale parameter is t^2. We shall consider only this case (for others see Problem 19). Let
$$F(x, t) = P\{W(t) \le x\}, \qquad G(y, x) = P\{T_t(x) \le y\}, \tag{131}$$
$$E(x) = 0 \quad \text{for } x < 1,$$
$$= 1 \quad \text{for } x \ge 1. \tag{132}$$

Theorem 22. *If $\rho_1 = 1$ and $\sigma^2 < \infty$, then*
$$\lim_{t \to \infty} P\left\{\frac{\sigma_1^2 W_0(t)}{\rho_0^2 t^2} \le y\right\} = G_{1/2}(y). \tag{133}$$

PROOF. Since $\rho_0 + \rho_1 > 1$ we see from Theorem 11 that $W(t)/t \to \rho_0 + \rho_1 - 1 = \rho_0$ in distribution. Therefore $F(\rho_0 ty, t) \to E(y)$ as $t \to \infty$. Using Theorem 8 we find that
$$P\left\{\frac{\sigma_1^2 W_0(t)}{\rho_0^2 t^2} \le y\right\} = P\left\{T_t[W(t)] \le \frac{\rho_0^2 t^2}{\sigma_1^2} y\right\}$$
$$= \int_{0-}^{\infty} F(dx, t) G\left(\frac{\rho_0^2 t^2}{\sigma_1^2} y, x\right)$$
$$= \int_{0-}^{\infty} F(\rho_0 t \, du, t) G\left(\frac{\rho_0^2 t^2 u^2}{\sigma_1^2} \cdot \frac{y}{u^2}, \rho_0 tu\right)$$
$$\to \int_{0-}^{\infty} E(du) G_{1/2}\left(\frac{y}{u^2}\right) = G_{1/2}(y). \qquad \square$$

11 Queues with Dynamic Priorities

In this section we consider the single-server queueing system in which the arrival processes and service time distributions are as described in the preceding section, but the queue discipline is of the *dynamic priority* type, described as follows: We associate the number u_0 with customers of class 0 and the number u_1 with those of class 1, such that if a customer of class i arrives at time t, he is assigned the number $t + u_i$ $(i = 0, 1)$. Here

$$-\infty \leq u_1 \leq u_0 \leq \infty. \tag{134}$$

If service is about to commence at any time, the server selects for service the customer with the minimum value of $t + u_i$ from among those present at that time. Under the head-of-the-line priority the customer so selected will continue to get served, while under the pre-emptive priority the system is continually monitored so that the customer receiving service at any time has the minimum value of $t_i + u_i$ out of all customers present at that time. In the latter case a pre-empted customer will resume his service from where it was interrupted. Thus the queue discipline is equivalent to a scheduling rule based on *earliest due dates* (EDD).

Let $\mathscr{A}_t$ be the set of arrival epochs of customers present at time t, and consider the expression

$$\min_{\substack{t' \in \mathscr{A}_t, \\ i=0, 1}} \{t' + u_i\} = \min\{\min(t'_0 + u_0), \min(t'_1 + u_1)\}, \tag{135}$$

where t'_i is the arrival epoch of a class i customer and $t'_i \in \mathscr{A}_t$ $(i = 0, 1)$. Now let C_i be the earliest among class i arrivals who are present at time t, and t''_i his arrival epoch. Then we can write this last expression as

$$\min\{t''_0 + u_0, t''_1 + u_1\}. \tag{136}$$

Thus in each class the queue discipline is first come, first served, and moreover, C_1 will get priority over C_0 iff $t''_1 + u_1 < t''_0 + u_0$, or

$$t''_1 < t''_0 + u, \tag{137}$$

where $u = u_0 - u_1 \geq 0$. From (137) we find that if $u = 0$ the queue discipline reduces to first come–first served, whereas if $u = \infty$, it reduces to static priorities. Thus the EDD queue discipline is a generalization of these two disciplines.

Let $W_i(t)$ be the virtual waiting time of a customer of class i $(i = 0, 1)$. We define the processes $W_i(t')$ and the random variable $T_t(w)$ as in the preceding section. We have then the following results.

Theorem 23. *The virtual waiting time $W_0(t)$ is given by*

$$W_0(t) = \min\{T_t(w), u + W_t(u)\}, \tag{138}$$

where $w = W(t)$, the total remaining workload at time t, and $W_t(t')$ is defined by (124) with $W_t(0) = w$.

PROOF. Consider a customer C_0 of class 0 arriving at time t. Then C_0 has to wait (i) for all (class 0 and class 1) customers present at time t, and (ii) for class 1 customers who arrive during $(t, t + u]$. Thus $W_0(t) \geq W(t)$.

If $T_t(w) \le u$, then C_0 commences service at time $t + T_t(w)$, so that $W_0(t) = T_t(w)$. If $T_t(w) > u$, then C_0 has to wait for $u+$ remaining workload (in respect of class 1 customers) at time $t + u$, initiated by a workload at time t. In this case

$$W_0(t) = u + W_t(u).$$

Now if $T_t(w) > u$ we have from (124) $W_t(t') > 0$ $(0 \le t' \le u)$ and

$$u + W_t(u) = w + X_1(t + u) - X_1(t)$$
$$\le w + X_1[t + T_t(w)] - X_1(t) = T_t(w).$$

Combining all these results we obtain (138). □

Theorem 24. *We have*

$$W_0(t) = \min\{T_t(w), u + W_1(t + u)\}. \tag{139}$$

PROOF. Consider a customer C_1 of class 1 arriving at time $t + u$. Then C_1 has to wait (i) for all (class 0 and class 1) customers present at time t, and (ii) for all class 1 customers who arrive during $(t, t + u]$. If $T_t(w) > u$, then $W_1(t + u) = W_t(u)$ for both pre-emptive resume and head-of-the-line queue disciplines, and by Theorem 23, $W_0(t) = u + W_t(u)$. Therefore

$$W_0(t) = u + W_1(t + u) \quad \text{if } T_t(w) > u.$$

Let $T_t(w) \le u$. Then in the case of pre-emptive resume discipline, $W_1(t + u) = W_t(u)$, whereas in the head-of-the-line case, owing to possible interruptions from class 0 customers, $W_1(t + u) \ge W_t(u)$. Thus by Theorem 23 we have

$$W_0(t) = T_t(w) \le u \le u + W_1(t + u) \quad \text{if } T_t(w) \le u.$$

The result (139) is therefore completely proved. □

Remarks. (a) As already noted, the case $u = 0$ corresponds to the first come, first served queue discipline. Theorem 23 gives

$$W_0(t) = \min\{T_t(w), w\} = w,$$

since $T_t(w) \ge w$. Thus $W_0(t) = w = W(t)$, as it should be. If $u = \infty$, Theorem 24 gives

$$W_0(t) = T_t(w), \quad w = W(t),$$

in agreement with Theorem 21 for static priorities.

(b) The limit distributions of $W_i(t)$ $(i = 0, 1)$ can be obtained from (139) in the usual manner. We note from (139) in particular that

$$P\{u < W_0(t) \le x\} = P\{W_0(t) > u, W_1(t + u) \le x - u\}. \tag{140}$$

In the limit as $t \to \infty$ this relation shows that a new arrival of class 1 will be in about the same statistical situation as customers of class 0 who have already waited for u units of time.

Problems

1. When $X(t)$ has the gamma density of example (3) of section 2, show that
$$\eta_0 = 2(\rho - 1) + o(\rho - 1) \qquad (\rho \to 1-).$$

2. For the generalized storage model of section 3, show that
$$\int_0^\infty e^{-st} E[e^{-\theta Z(t)}; Z(\tau) > 0 \ (0 \le \tau \le t) | Z(0) = x] \, dt = \frac{e^{-\theta x} - e^{-\eta x}}{s - \theta + \phi(\theta)}$$
$$(\theta > 0, s > 0).$$

3. Derive the results
$$ET(x) = x(1 - \rho)^{-1}, \qquad \text{Var } T(x) = x\sigma^2(1 - \rho)^{-3}$$
by using the Wald equation for stopping times.

4. For the next input process $Y(t)$, let
$$M(t) = \frac{e^{-\theta Y(t)}}{E[e^{-\theta Y(t)}]}.$$

(i) Establish the martingale property
$$E[M(t + t') | M(s) \ (0 \le s \le t)] = M(t) \qquad (t' \ge 0, t \ge 0).$$

(ii) Use this property to prove that
$$Ee^{-sT(x)} = e^{-x\eta(s)}.$$

5. If the input $X(t)$ has mean $\rho = 1$ and variance $\sigma^2 < \infty$, show that
$$P\{T(x) > t\} \sim \sqrt{\frac{2}{\pi}} \cdot \frac{x}{\sigma} t^{-1/2} \qquad (t \to \infty).$$

6. If the input $X(t)$ is an inverse Gaussian process with density
$$k(x, t) = \frac{t}{\sigma\sqrt{2\pi}} \left(\frac{\rho}{x}\right)^{3/2} e^{-(\rho/2\sigma^2 x)(x - \rho t)^2},$$
show that the process $\{T(x), x \ge 0\}$ is also inverse Gaussian with unit drift. In particular, when $\rho = 1$, show that the random variable $\sigma^2[T(x) - x]x^{-2}$ has the stable density with exponent $\frac{1}{2}$.

7. In the queueing system M/G/1 with $\rho = 1$ and $\sigma^2 < \infty$, show that
$$\lim_{n \to \infty} P\left\{\frac{\lambda^2 \sigma^2 T_n}{n^2} \le x\right\} = G_{1/2}(x)$$

8. Let the queueing system M/G/1 be initially empty.

(i) Prove that
$$P\{I(t) < x\} = 1 - \sum_{n=0}^\infty e^{-\lambda x} \frac{(\lambda x)^n}{n!} G_n(t - x),$$
where $G_n(t)$ is the d.f. of T_n $(n \ge 1)$ and $G_0(t) = 0$ for $t < 0$, and $= 1$ for $t \ge 0$.

(ii) Use this result to show that
$$\lim_{t\to\infty} P\{I(t) < x\} = 0 \qquad \text{if } \rho \le 1$$
$$= 1 - e^{-\eta_0 x} \qquad \text{if } \rho > 1.$$

9. In the generalized storage model of section 3, prove that as $t \to \infty$, the ratio $I(t)/t \to 1 - \rho$ if $\rho < 1$, and $\to 0$ if $\rho \ge 1$.

10. For $F(x; 0, t)$ defined by (84), show that if $\rho = 1$ and $\sigma^2 < \infty$
$$\lim_{t\to\infty} t^{1/2} F(\sigma x \sqrt{t}; 0, t) = \frac{\sigma}{\sqrt{2\pi}} e^{-x^2/2} \qquad (x \ge 0).$$

11. For the process $Y(t)$ show that the ascending ladder height $Y(T^*)$ has density $M^+_{\eta_0}(x)$, where
$$M^+_{\eta_0}(x) = \int_x^\infty e^{-\eta_0(y-x)} \frac{M(dy)}{y^2} \qquad (x > 0).$$

12. If $\rho < 1$, show that the d.f. of $M = \lim_{t\to\infty} M(t)$ can be written as
$$P\{M \le x\} = (1 - \rho) \sum_{k=0}^\infty P\{Y(T^*_k) \le x\},$$
where T^*_k ($k \ge 0$) are the ladder epochs of the process $Y(t)$.

13. Continuation. Show that if $\rho < 1$ and $\sigma^2 < \infty$,
$$\lim_{\rho \to 1^-} P\left\{\frac{2(1-\rho)}{\sigma^2} M > x\right\} = e^{-x}.$$
[Note that the limit distribution of $Z(t)$ as $t \to \infty$ is the same as that of the random variable M.]

14. For the storage model of section 8, prove the following:

(i) Let T^*_1 be the time to first overflow, that is,
$$T^*_1 = \inf\{t > 0 : \bar{Z}(t) = c\}.$$
Show that
$$P\{T^*_1 \le t\} = 1 - F(0; c - x, t) \qquad (x \le c, t > 0).$$

(ii) The d.f. of $\bar{Z}(t)$ before overflow is given by
$$P\{\bar{Z}(t) \le z, \bar{Z}(\tau) < c \ (0 \le \tau \le t) | \bar{Z}(0) = x\}$$
$$= F(c - z; c - x, t) \qquad (z < c, x \le c, t > 0),$$
where $F(x; y, t) = P\{Z(t) \le y | Z(0) = x\}$, $Z(t)$ being the process described in section 3.

15. For the storage model of section 8, prove that

(i) if $\rho < 1$ and $\sigma^2 < \infty$, then
$$\lim_{t\to\infty} P\left\{\frac{\bar{Z}(t) - (\rho - 1)t}{\sigma \sqrt{t}} \le x\right\} = N(x).$$

(ii) if $\rho = 1$ and $\sigma^2 < \infty$, then

$$\lim_{t \to \infty} P\left\{\frac{\bar{Z}(t)}{\sigma\sqrt{t}} \le x\right\} = N_-(x).$$

[Note: Similar results hold for $\bar{I}(t)$.]

16. In the queueing system G/M/1 with $\bar{\rho} = 1$ and $\sigma^2 < \infty$, show that

$$\lim_{t \to \infty} P\left\{\frac{\bar{W}(t)}{\sigma\sqrt{t}} < x\right\} = N_+(x).$$

[Hint: Use the result of Problem 10.]

17. In the priority queueing model of section 10 we shall say that the system is busy as long as customers of either low or high priority are present. For $(m, n) \ne (0, 0)$, let T_{mn} be the busy period which commences with m low priority and n high priority customers, with a service just starting. Prove the following:

(i) $E(e^{-sT_{mn}}) = \psi_0(\eta)^m \psi_1(\eta)^n$, where $\eta \equiv \eta(s)$ is given by (121).
(ii) $T_{mn} < \infty$ with probability one iff $\rho_0 + \rho_1 \le 1$.
(iii) $E(T_{mn}) = \dfrac{m\rho_0}{\lambda_0(1 - \rho_0 - \rho_1)} + \dfrac{n\rho_1}{\lambda_1(1 - \rho_0 - \rho_1)}$ if $\rho_0 + \rho_1 < 1$.
(iv) For the busy cycle (idle period + busy period) we have

$$E(Z) = [(\lambda_0 + \lambda_1)(1 - \rho_0 - \rho_1)]^{-1} \quad \text{if } \rho_0 + \rho_1 < 1.$$

18. In the priority queueing model of section 10, let us denote by V the time during which a low priority customer's service is blocked by the low priority customer immediately ahead of him and the interruptions that occur; V is called the completion time. Prove the following:

(i) $E(e^{-\theta V}) = \psi_0(\eta_1)$, where $\eta_1 \equiv \eta_1(\theta)$ is given by (128).
(ii) $V < \infty$ with probability one iff $\rho_1 \le 1$.
(iii) $E(V) = \rho_0[\lambda_0(1 - \rho_1)]^{-1}$ if $\rho_1 < 1$, and $= \infty$ if $\rho_1 = 1$.

19. For the process $W_0(t)$ of section 10, prove the following:

(i) If $\rho_0 + \rho_1 < 1$ and $\sigma^2 < \infty$, then the limit distribution of $W_0(t)$ has the mean

$$\frac{\sigma^2}{2(1 - \rho_0 - \rho_1)(1 - \rho_1)}.$$

(ii) If $\rho_0 + \rho_1 > 1$, $\rho_1 < 1$ and $\sigma^2 < \infty$, then

$$\lim_{t \to \infty} P\left\{\frac{W_0(t) - m_2 t}{\sigma_2 \sqrt{t}} \le y\right\} = N(y),$$

where

$$m_2 = \frac{\rho_0 + \rho_1 - 1}{1 - \rho_1}, \qquad \sigma_2^2 = \frac{\sigma_0^2(1 - \rho_1) + \sigma_1^2 \rho_0}{(1 - \rho_1)^3}.$$

(iii) If $\rho_0 + \rho_1 = 1$, $\sigma^2 < \infty$, then

$$\lim_{t \to \infty} P\left\{\frac{\rho_0 W_0(t)}{\sigma\sqrt{t}} \le y\right\} = N_+(y).$$

20. In the queueing model of section 11, show that a class 0 customer's waiting time is greater than what it would be under the first come, first served discipline, but less than what it would be under the priority discipline of section 10.

Chapter 4

More Storage Models

1 Introduction

In the preceding chapter we investigated storage models in which the net input process Y was of the form $Y(t) = X(t) - t$, X being a non-negative Lévy process. Although such an input would seem to be rather special, we found it to be appropriate for a wide variety of situations, in particular, for queues with first come, first served discipline as well as queues with priorities. However, there still remains the general case of the insurance risk problem and the simple queue in which the net input is of the form $Y(t) = A(t) - D(t)$, with A, D two independent simple Poisson processes. In order to investigate these and further storage models we need to develop some new concepts concerning Lévy processes. Accordingly, let Y be a Levy process with the c.f.

$$Ee^{i\omega Y(t)} = e^{-t\phi(\omega)}, \tag{1}$$

where $\phi(\omega)$ is as given in Chapter 3, Section 2. Let us define the random variables

$$T = \inf\{t: Y(t) > 0\}, \qquad \bar{T} = \inf\{t: Y(t) < 0\}. \tag{2}$$

Our immediate concern here is whether or not these random variables are > 0 a.s. The following is true:

Theorem 1. *The random variables $T > 0$, $\bar{T} > 0$ a.s. iff Y is a compound Poisson process with zero drift.*

PROOF. Let $T_0 = \min(T, \bar{T})$. We have

$$P\{T_0 > t\} = P\{Y(s) = 0 \ (0 \leq s \leq t)\} = g(t) \qquad \text{(say)}. \tag{3}$$

1 Introduction

(i) Since a Lévy process is also Markov, we have
$$g(t) = e^{-\lambda t},$$
with $0 < \lambda \le \infty$. If $T_0 > 0$ a.s., then we must have
$$\lim_{t \to 0+} g(t) = 1.$$
This gives $\lambda < \infty$, and therefore Y is a compound Poisson process with zero drift.

(ii) Let Y be a compound Poisson process with zero drift. Then $g(t) = e^{-\lambda t}$ with $0 < \lambda < \infty$, and $g(t) \to 1$ as $t \to 0$. This gives $T_0 > 0$ a.s., and the proof is complete. □

Remarks. (a) For the Brownian motion Y we have
$$\limsup_{t \to 0+} \frac{Y(t)}{t} = +\infty, \quad \liminf_{t \to 0+} \frac{Y(t)}{t} = -\infty. \tag{4}$$
This shows that $T = \bar{T} = 0$ a.s. It turns out that (4) is true for any Lévy process Y with unbounded variation, so for such processes $T = \bar{T} = 0$ a.s.

(b) Let Y be a Lévy process with bounded variation and drift d. We shall prove below that
$$\text{if } d < 0, \quad T > 0 \quad \text{a.s.,}$$
$$\text{if } d > 0, \quad \bar{T} > 0 \quad \text{a.s.}$$
If the drift is zero, no general conclusion is possible. We have already seen that if Y is a compound Poisson with zero drift, then $T > 0$, $\bar{T} > 0$ a.s. On the other hand, let Y be a symmetric stable process with exponent $\alpha < 1$. This is of bounded variation and has drift zero. Because of symmetry we must clearly have $T = \bar{T} = 0$ a.s.

Theorem 2. *Let Y be a Lévy process with bounded variation and drift d. Then (i) if $d < 0$, $T > 0$ a.s., and (ii) if $d > 0$, $\bar{T} > 0$ a.s.*

PROOF. It suffices to prove (i). It is known that
$$\lim_{t \to 0+} \frac{Y(t)}{t} = d \quad \text{a.s.} \tag{5}$$
Therefore there exists a $t(\omega)$ such that
$$\frac{Y(s, \omega)}{s} < \frac{1}{2}d < 0 \quad \text{for } 0 < s \le t(\omega)$$
for almost all ω. Let
$$t_0 \equiv t_0(\omega) = \sup\{t: Y(s, \omega) < 0 \quad (0 < s \le t)\}. \tag{6}$$
Then $t_0 > 0$ a.s., which means that $T > t_0 > 0$, as required. □

We shall denote by $\mathscr{L}_+$ the class of Lévy processes for which $T > 0$ a.s., and $\mathscr{L}_-$ the class for which $\bar{T} > 0$ a.s. Theorems 1 and 2 show that $\mathscr{L}_+$ includes Lévy processes with bounded variation and drift $d < 0$, but is a proper subclass of those with drift ≤ 0. A similar remark applies to $\mathscr{L}_-$. The distribution of the ladder points for processes of class $\mathscr{L}_+ \cup \mathscr{L}_-$ is given by the following theorem. □

Theorem 3. (a) *If* $Y \in \mathscr{L}_+$, *then*

$$E[e^{-sT+i\omega Y(T)}] = 1 - \exp\left\{-\int_0^\infty t^{-1} e^{-st} E[e^{i\omega Y(t)}; Y(t) > 0]\, dt\right\}. \quad (7)$$

(b) *If* $Y \in \mathscr{L}_-$, *then*

$$E[e^{-s\bar{T}+i\omega Y(\bar{T})}] = 1 - \exp\left\{-\int_0^\infty t^{-1} e^{-st} E[e^{i\omega Y(t)}; Y(t) < 0]\, dt\right\}. \quad (8)$$

Here $s > 0$ *and* ω *is real.* □

We shall prove this theorem only in the case where

$$Y(t) = X_1(t) - X_2(t) - \beta t, \quad (9)$$

with $X_1 \geq 0$, $X_2 \geq 0$, and at least one of X_1, X_2 is a compound Poisson process (Theorem 6). Since every process in the class $\mathscr{L}_+ \cup \mathscr{L}_-$ can be expressed as the limit of a sequence of processes of this type, Theorem 6 will then lead to Theorem 3. However, we shall not demonstrate this fact here. Properties of processes in the class $\mathscr{L}_+ \cup \mathscr{L}_-$ are investigated in section 4, and used to solve the insurance risk problem in the general case (section 5) and to study the M/M/1 queue (section 6). A storage model with random output is investigated in section 7.

In order to prove Theorem 6 we first consider in section 2 a random walk in the upper half plane and establish results concerning the ladder points of this random walk.

In view of Theorem 1 we expect a Wiener–Hopf factorization to hold only for compound Poisson processes with zero drift. Since the inequalities in (2) are both strong, this factorization assumes a symmetric form (by contrast the factorization for random walks investigated in chapters 1 and 2 are nonsymmetric). We have the following:

Theorem 4. *For a compound Poisson process* Y *with zero drift and c.f. given by* (1) *we have the factorization*

$$r_0(s)[s + \phi(\omega)] = [1 - E(e^{-sT+i\omega Y(T)})][1 - E(e^{-s\bar{T}+i\omega Y(\bar{T})})], \quad (10)$$

where

$$sr_0(s) = \exp\left\{-\int_0^\infty t^{-1} e^{-st} P\{Y(t) \neq 0\}\, dt\right\}. \quad (11)$$

PROOF. From Theorem 3 we obtain

$$[1 - E(e^{-sT+i\omega Y(T)})][1 - E(e^{-s\bar{T}+i\omega Y(\bar{T})})],$$

$$= \exp\left\{-\int_0^\infty t^{-1}e^{-st}E[e^{i\omega Y(t)}; Y(t) \neq 0]\,dt\right\}$$

$$= \exp\left\{-\int_0^\infty t^{-1}e^{-st}E[e^{i\omega Y(t)} - 1]\,dt\right\} \cdot \exp\left\{-\int_0^\infty t^{-1}e^{-st}P\{Y(t) \neq 0\}\,dt\right\}.$$

This leads to the desired result (10) since

$$\int_0^\infty t^{-1}e^{-st}P\{Y(t) \neq 0\}\,dt \leq \int_0^\infty t^{-1}e^{-st}(1 - e^{-vt})\,dt = \log\frac{v+s}{v} < \infty,$$

where v $(0 < v < \infty)$ is the jump rate of the process, and

$$\int_0^\infty t^{-1}e^{-st}E[e^{i\omega Y(t)} - 1]\,dt = \int_0^\infty t^{-1}e^{-st}[e^{-t\phi(\omega)} - 1]\,dt = \log\frac{s}{s + \phi(\omega)}.$$

$\square$

2 Ladder Points for a Two-Dimensional Random Walk

Let $\{(\tau_k, X_k), k \geq 1\}$ be a sequence of independent random variables with a common distribution, and let $T_0 \equiv S_0 \equiv 0$, $T_n = \tau_1 + \tau_2 + \cdots + \tau_n$, $S_n = X_1 + X_2 + \cdots + X_n$ $(n \geq 1)$. Then $\{(T_n, S_n), n \geq 0\}$ is a random walk in two dimensions. We seek to develop a fluctuation theory for this random walk in the special case where the random variables τ_k are nonnegative. If we denote the common distribution of (τ_k, X_k) as $F(d\tau, dx)$, then $F(d\tau, dx)$ is concentrated on $[0, \infty) \times (-\infty, \infty)$. As $\{T_n\}$ is a nondecreasing sequence, the ladder epochs of this random walk are appropriately defined as

$$N = \min\{n: S_n > 0\}, \quad \bar{N} = \min\{n: S_n < 0\}, \tag{12}$$

where for the purpose of future applications we use strong inequalities. The corresponding ladder points are then

$$(N, T_N, S_N) \quad \text{and} \quad (\bar{N}, T_{\bar{N}}, S_{\bar{N}}). \tag{13}$$

We are interested only in (T_N, S_N) and $(T_{\bar{N}}, S_{\bar{N}})$.

Theorem 5. *For $s > 0$, ω real we have*

$$E(e^{-sT_N + i\omega S_N}) = 1 - \exp\left\{-\sum_1^\infty \frac{1}{n}E[e^{-sT_n + i\omega S_n}; S_n > 0]\right\} \tag{14}$$

$$E(e^{-sT_{\bar{N}} + i\omega S_{\bar{N}}}) = 1 - \exp\left\{-\sum_1^\infty \frac{1}{n}E[e^{-sT_n + i\omega S_n}; S_n < 0]\right\}. \tag{15}$$

PROOF. Let

$$K_s(dx) = \int_0^\infty e^{-s\tau} F(d\tau, dx). \tag{16}$$

Then K_s is a probability distribution. For the random walk $\{S_{ns}, n \geq 0\}$ induced by K_s, let (N_s, S_{N_s}) be the first ascending ladder point. For $n \geq 1$, $x > 0$ we have then

$P\{N_s = n, S_{N_s} \in dx\}$

$$= \int e^{-s(\tau_1 + \tau_2 + \cdots + \tau_n)} F(d\tau_1, dx_1) F(d\tau_2, dx_2) \cdots F(d\tau_n, dx_n),$$

the integral being taken over the region $\tau_i \geq 0$ ($i = 1, 2, \ldots, n$), $x_1 \leq 0$, $x_1 + x_2 \leq 0$, $\ldots$, $x_1 + x_2 + \cdots + x_{n-1} \leq 0$, $x_1 + x_2 + \cdots + x_n \in dx$. Clearly, the value of this integral

$$= E[e^{-sT_N}; N = n, S_N \in dx]$$

and so

$$E(e^{-sT_N + i\omega S_N}) = E[\exp(i\omega S_{N_s})] \tag{17}$$
$$= 1 - \exp\left\{-\sum_1^\infty \frac{1}{n} E[e^{i\omega S_{ns}}; S_{ns} > 0]\right\},$$

where we have used equation (6) of chapter 2. From (16) we see that the n-fold convolution of K_s with itself is given by

$$K_{sn}(dx) = \int_0^\infty e^{-st} F_n(dt, dx),$$

where F_n is the n-fold convolution of F with itself. Therefore

$$E[e^{i\omega S_{ns}}; S_{ns} > 0] = E[e^{-sT_n + i\omega S_n}; S_n > 0]. \tag{18}$$

The result (14) follows from (17) and (18). The proof of (15) is similar. □

3 Ladder Points for Processes of Class $\mathscr{L}_+$

We consider Lévy processes of the type

$$Y(t) = X_1(t) - X_2(t) - \beta t, \tag{19}$$

where X_1 is a compound Poisson process on $[0, \infty)$, X_2 a Lévy process with nondecreasing sample functions and $\beta \geq 0$. For this process $T > 0$ a.s. The distribution of $\{T, Y(T)\}$ is given by the following:

Theorem 6. *For the process Y defined by (19) we have*

$$E[e^{-sT + i\omega Y(T)}] = 1 - \exp\left\{-\int_0^\infty t^{-1} e^{-st} E[e^{i\omega Y(t)}; Y(t) > 0]\, dt\right\} \tag{20}$$

for $s > 0$, ω real.

PROOF. Let X_1 be determined by the jump rate v and jump size distribution B. Also, let $G(t, x)$ be the d.f. of $X_2(t)$. Let $T_0 \equiv 0$, T_n $(n \geq 1)$ the epoch of the nth jump in X_1, and $S_n = Y(T_n)$. Then the sequence of random variables $\{(T_n, S_n), n \geq 0\}$ is a random walk, since the increments

$$T_n - T_{n-1}, \qquad S_n - S_{n-1}$$

are independent random variables with the common distribution

$$F(d\tau, dx) = ve^{-v\tau} d\tau \int_0^\infty dB(v) G(\tau, v - \beta\tau - dx). \tag{21}$$

The distribution of (T_n, S_n) is therefore given by

$$F_n(dt, dx) = v^n e^{-vt} \frac{t^{n-1}}{(n-1)!} dt \int_0^\infty dB_n(v) G(t, v - \beta t - dx). \tag{22}$$

For the random walk $\{(T_n, S_n)\}$ let N be the first ascending ladder epoch as defined in section 2. Then clearly $T = T_N$, $Y(T) = S_N$, and therefore Theorem 5 gives the desired result since

$$\sum_1^\infty \frac{1}{n} E[e^{-sT_n + i\omega S_n}; S_n > 0]$$

$$= \sum_1^\infty \frac{1}{n} \int_0^\infty \int_{0+}^\infty e^{-st + i\omega x} F_n(dt, dx)$$

$$= \sum_1^\infty \frac{1}{n} \int_0^\infty \int_{0+}^\infty e^{-st + i\omega x} v^n e^{-vt} \frac{t^{n-1}}{(n-1)!} dt \int_0^\infty dB_n(v) G(t, v - \beta t - dx)$$

$$= \int_0^\infty \int_{0+}^\infty t^{-1} e^{-st + i\omega x} P\{Y(t) \in dx, N(t) > 0\} dt$$

$$= \int_0^\infty t^{-1} e^{-st} E[e^{i\omega Y(t)}; Y(t) > 0, N(t) > 0] dt,$$

where $N(t)$ is the number of jumps in X_1 during the interval $(0, t]$ and we note that $N(t) = 0$ implies $Y(t) = -X_2(t) - \beta t \leq 0$. □

4 Properties of Processes of Class $\mathscr{L}_+ \cup \mathscr{L}_-$

As for the models of chapter 3 we are interested in the functionals

$$M(t) = \sup_{0 \leq \tau \leq t} Y(\tau), \qquad m(t) = \inf_{0 \leq \tau \leq t} Y(\tau). \tag{23}$$

If at least one of the random variables T, $\bar{T}$ is > 0 a.s., then the distribution of M and m can be obtained using Theorem 3. We first need the following results, which are stated for processes of class $\mathscr{L}_+$. Let

$$T_0 \equiv 0, \qquad T_k = \inf\{t: Y(t) - Y(T_{k-1}) > 0\} \qquad (k \geq 1). \tag{24}$$

We call T_k the kth ascending ladder epoch and $Y(T_k)$ the corresponding ladder height. It is clear that the random variables

$$\{T_k - T_{k-1}, Y(T_k) - Y(T_{k-1}), k \geq 1\} \tag{25}$$

are independently and identically distributed. Their common distribution is given by (7). For the random walk $\{T_k, Y(T_k)\}$ we define the transforms

$$u^*(s, \omega) = \sum_{k=0}^{\infty} E[e^{-sT_k + i\omega Y(T_k)}], \tag{26}$$

$$v^*(s, \omega) = \int_0^{\infty} e^{-st} E[e^{i\omega Y(t)}; T > t] \, dt, \tag{27}$$

for $s > 0$, ω real. We have then the following:

Lemma 1. *Let Y be a Lévy process belonging to the class $\mathscr{L}_+$. Then*

$$u^*(s, \omega) = \exp\left\{\int_0^{\infty} t^{-1} e^{-st} E[e^{i\omega Y(t)}; Y(t) > 0] \, dt\right\} \tag{28}$$

and

$$v^*(s, \omega) = [s + \phi(\omega)]^{-1} u^*(s, \omega)^{-1}. \tag{29}$$

PROOF. We have

$$u^*(s, \omega) = [1 - E(e^{-sT + i\omega Y(T)})]^{-1}$$

and in view of (7), this leads to (28). Also, proceeding as in the proof of Theorem 9 of chapter 3, we obtain

$$\frac{1 - E[e^{-sT + i\omega Y(T)}]}{s + \phi(\omega)} = v^*(s, \omega)$$

which leads to (29). □

Theorem 7. *For a Lévy process Y in the class $\mathscr{L}_+ \cup \mathscr{L}_-$ we have*

$$s \int_0^{\infty} e^{-st} E[e^{i\omega_1 M(t) + i\omega_2 [M(t) - Y(t)]}] \, dt = \exp\left\{\int_0^{\infty} (e^{i\omega_1 y} - 1) v_s(dy)\right. \tag{30}$$

$$\left. + \int_{-\infty}^0 (e^{-i\omega_2 y} - 1) v_s(dy)\right\} \quad (s > 0, \omega_1, \omega_2 \text{ real}),$$

where v_s is the Lévy measure

$$v_s\{0\} = 0, \quad v_s(dy) = \int_0^{\infty} t^{-1} e^{-st} F(t, dy) \, dt \quad (y \neq 0), \tag{31}$$

$F(t, A)$ being the distribution measure of $Y(t)$.

4 Properties of Processes of Class $\mathscr{L}_+ \cup \mathscr{L}_-$

PROOF. (i) Let $Y \in \mathscr{L}_+$. Then $T > 0$ a.s. and

$$P\{M(t) \in dx, M(t) - Y(t) \in dy\}$$

$$= \sum_{k=0}^{\infty} P\{M(t) \in dx, M(t) - Y(t) \in dy, T_k \leq t < T_{k+1}\}$$

$$= \sum_{k=0}^{\infty} \int_0^t P\{T_k \in d\tau, Y(T_k) \in dx\}.$$

$$P\{Y(T_k) - Y(t) \in dy, T_{k+1} > t \mid T_k = \tau, Y(T_k) = x\}$$

$$= \sum_{k=0}^{\infty} \int_0^t P\{T_k \in d\tau, Y(T_k) \in dx\} P\{Y(t-\tau) \in -dy, T_1 > t - \tau\}.$$

Therefore

$$\int_0^\infty e^{-st} E[e^{i\omega_1 M(t) + i\omega_2[M(t) - Y(t)]}] \, dt$$

$$= \sum_{k=0}^{\infty} E[e^{-sT_k + i\omega_1 Y(T_k)}] \cdot \int_0^\infty e^{-st} E[e^{-i\omega_2 Y(t)}; T_1 > t] \, dt \quad (32)$$

$$= u^*(s, \omega_1) v^*(s, -\omega_2).$$

Also, putting $\omega_1 = \omega_2 = 0$ in this we obtain

$$s^{-1} = u^*(s, 0) v^*(s, 0). \quad (33)$$

Using (32), (33) and Lemma 1, we find that the left side of (30) is equal to

$$\frac{u^*(s, \omega_1)}{u^*(s, 0)} \cdot \frac{s}{s + \phi(-\omega_2)} \cdot \frac{u^*(s, 0)}{u^*(s, -\omega_2)}$$

$$= \exp\left\{\int_0^\infty t^{-1} e^{-st} E[(e^{i\omega_1 Y(t)} - 1); Y(t) > 0] \, dt\right\}$$

$$\times \exp\left\{\int_0^\infty t^{-1} e^{-st} E(e^{-i\omega_2 Y(t)} - 1) \, dt\right.$$

$$\left. - \int_0^\infty t^{-1} e^{-st} E[(e^{-i\omega_2 Y(t)} - 1); Y(t) > 0] \, dt\right\}$$

$$= \exp\left\{\int_0^\infty t^{-1} e^{-st} E[(e^{i\omega_1 Y(t)} - 1); Y(t) > 0] \, dt\right\}$$

$$\times \exp\left\{\int_0^\infty t^{-1} e^{-st} E[(e^{-i\omega_2 Y(t)} - 1); Y(t) < 0] \, dt\right\},$$

and this last expression can be written in the desired form.

(ii) Let $Y \in \mathscr{L}_-$. Then $\bar{T} > 0$ a.s. and

$$E[e^{-s\bar{T} + i\omega Y(\bar{T})}] = 1 - \exp\left\{\int_0^\infty t^{-1} e^{-st} E[e^{i\omega Y(t)}; Y(t) < 0] \, dt\right\}$$

from (8). Proceeding as in case (i) we find that

$$s \int_0^\infty e^{-st} E[e^{i\omega_1[Y(t)-m(t)]+i\omega_2 m(t)}] \, dt$$
$$= \exp\left\{\int_{-\infty}^0 (e^{i\omega_2 y} - 1) v_s(dy) + \int_0^\infty (e^{i\omega_1 y} - 1) v_s(dy)\right\},$$

and so the desired result holds also for $\mathscr{L}_-$, since by Lemma 1 of chapter 3 we have

$$\{Y(t) - m(t), -m(t)\} \sim \{M(t), M(t) - Y(t)\}. \qquad \square$$

Theorem 8. *For $Y \in \mathscr{L}_+ \cup \mathscr{L}_-$ we have*

$$s \int_0^\infty e^{-st} E[e^{i\omega M(t)}] \, dt = \exp\left\{\int_0^\infty (e^{i\omega y} - 1) v_s(dy)\right\} \qquad (s > 0, I_m(\omega) \geq 0) \quad (34)$$

and

$$s \int_0^\infty e^{-st} E[e^{i\omega m(t)}] \, dt = \exp\left\{\int_{-\infty}^0 (e^{i\omega y} - 1) v_s(dy)\right\} \qquad (s > 0, I_m(\omega) \leq 0). \quad (35)$$

PROOF. Setting $\omega_1 = \omega$, $\omega_2 = 0$ in (30) we obtain (34). To prove (35) we recall from Lemma 1 of chapter 3 that $M(t) - Y(t) \sim -m(t)$. Therefore setting $\omega_1 = 0$, $\omega_2 = -\omega$ in (30) we obtain (35). $\qquad \square$

It is clear that in order to make full use of the Weiner–Hopf techniques of the type used in chapters 1 and 2, we have to restrict ourselves to the compound Poisson process Y with zero drift. The special case where Y has the state-space $\{\ldots, -1, 0, 1, 2, \ldots\}$ arises in queueing models. The p.g.f. of such a process is given by

$$E[z^{Y(t)}] = e^{-vt[1-C(z)]} \qquad (|z| = 1), \quad (36)$$

where $0 < v < \infty$ and $C(z) = \sum_{-\infty}^\infty c_n z^n$, $c_0 = 0$. The results established below will be used in section 6 for the study of the queueing system M/M/1.

We consider the case where

$$C(z) = pz + qz^{-1} \qquad (|z| = 1) \quad (37)$$

with $0 < p < 1$, $q = 1 - p$. The properties of the ladder epochs of this process can be described in terms of the roots of the equation $s + v - vC(z) = 0$ (for fixed $s > 0$), which reduces to

$$vpz^2 - (s + v)z + vq = 0. \quad (38)$$

The roots are given by $\xi \equiv \xi(s)$, $\eta \equiv \eta(s)$, where

$$\xi = \frac{s + v - \sqrt{(s+v)^2 - 4v^2 pq}}{2vp}, \quad (39)$$

$$\eta = \frac{s + v + \sqrt{(s+v)^2 - 4v^2 pq}}{2vp}. \quad (40)$$

We first note the following:

4 Properties of Processes of Class $\mathscr{L}_+ \cup \mathscr{L}_-$

Lemma 2. *For the quantities defined by* (39)–(40) *we have*
$$0 < \xi < 1 < \eta. \tag{41}$$

PROOF. From (38) we obtain
$$\xi + \eta = \frac{s+v}{vp}, \qquad \xi\eta = \frac{q}{p},$$
so that
$$(1-\xi)(\eta-1) = \xi + \eta - \xi\eta - 1 = \frac{s}{vp} > 0.$$

Therefore $1 - \xi$, $\eta - 1$ are of the same sign. Since $\xi < \eta$ we must have $\xi < 1$, $\eta > 1$, as desired. □

Theorem 9. (i) *For the ladder epochs T, $\bar{T}$ of the compound Poisson process defined by* (36)–(37) *we have*
$$E(e^{-sT}) = \eta^{-1}, \qquad E(e^{-s\bar{T}}) = \xi \qquad (s > 0). \tag{42}$$

(ii) *If $p = q$, then T and $\bar{T}$ are both proper random variables with $E(T) = E(\bar{T}) = \infty$.*
If $p > q$, then $\bar{T}$ is defective, while T is proper with
$$E(T) = [v(p-q)]^{-1}, \qquad \operatorname{Var}(T) = v^{-2}(p-q)^{-3}.$$
If $p > q$, then T is defective, while $\bar{T}$ is proper with
$$E(\bar{T}) = [v(q-p)]^{-1}, \qquad \operatorname{Var}(\bar{T}) = v^{-2}(q-p)^{-3}.$$

PROOF. We can write the Wiener–Hopf factorization (10) as
$$r_0(s)(s + v - vpz - vqz^{-1})$$
$$= [1 - E(e^{-sT}z^{Y(T)})][1 - E(e^{-s\bar{T}}z^{Y(\bar{T})})] \qquad (s > 0, |z| = 1). \tag{43}$$

Noting the inequalities (41) we can express the left side of (43) as
$$r_0(s)\frac{\mu}{\xi}\left(1 - \frac{z}{\eta}\right)\left(1 - \frac{\xi}{z}\right).$$

The uniqueness of the factorization (43) then yields the results
$$E[e^{-sT}z^{Y(T)}] = \frac{z}{\eta}, \qquad E[e^{-s\bar{T}}z^{Y(\bar{T})}] = \frac{\xi}{z}, \qquad r_0(s) = \frac{\xi}{\mu}. \tag{44}$$

These results confirm the obvious facts that $Y(T) \equiv 1$ and $Y(\bar{T}) \equiv -1$. We therefore obtain (42). The results in (ii) can be obtained in the usual manner from (39)–(40) by noting, for example, that
$$\xi(0+) = 1 \quad \text{if } p \le q,$$
$$= \frac{q}{p} \quad \text{if } p > q,$$
$$\xi'(0+) = -[v(q-p)]^{-1} \quad \text{if } p < q,$$
$$= -\infty \text{ if } p = q,$$
$$\xi''(0+) = v^{-2}(q-p)^{-3} \quad \text{if } p < q. \qquad \square$$

The supremum and infimum functionals of the process Y can be expressed in terms of the ladder epochs $\{T_j\}$ and $\{\bar{T}_j\}$. Thus

$$M(t) = \max\{j: T_j \le t\} \tag{45}$$

so that $M(t)$ is the number of renewals in the interval $(0, t]$ of the process $\{T_j, j \ge 0\}$. As an immediate consequence we have the following. Clearly, there is a similar result for $m(t)$.

Theorem 10. (i) *As* $t \to \infty$, $M(t) \to M \le \infty$, *where* $M < \infty$ *with probability one iff* $p < q$, *and*

$$P\{M \le j\} = 1 - \left(\frac{P}{q}\right)^j \quad (j \ge 0). \tag{46}$$

(ii) *If* $p > q$, *then*

$$\lim_{t \to \infty} P\left\{\frac{M(t) - v(p - q)t}{\sqrt{vt}} \le x\right\} = N(x). \tag{47}$$

(iii) *If* $p = q$, *then*

$$\lim_{t \to \infty} P\left\{\frac{M(t)}{\sqrt{vt}} < x\right\} = N_+(x). \tag{48}$$

PROOF. (i) Since $M(t)$ is nondecreasing in t, $M(t) \to M \le \infty$. From (45) we obtain

$$P\{M(t) \le j\} = P\{T_j \ge t\}, \tag{49}$$

so that

$$\lim_{t \to \infty} P\{M(t) \le j\} = P\{T_j = \infty\} = 1 - \left(\frac{P}{q}\right)^j.$$

(ii) If $p > q$, then random variables T_j are the partial sums of the sequence $T_1, T_2 - T_1, T_3 - T_2, \ldots$, which are independent and identically distributed with finite mean and variance, by Theorem 8(ii). Therefore the sequence $\{T_j\}$ obeys the central limit theorem, and the result (47) follows from (49) in the usual manner.

(iii) If $p = q$ we have from (40)

$$\eta^{-1}(s) = 1 - \frac{\sqrt{2s}}{v} + o(\sqrt{s}) \quad (s \to 0+),$$

so that

$$E(e^{-svT_j/j^2}) = \left[1 - \frac{\sqrt{2s}}{j} + o\left(\frac{1}{j}\right)\right]^j \to e^{-\sqrt{2s}}.$$

Proceeding as in the proof of Theorem 10 of chapter 3 we arrive at (48) and the proof is complete. □

Remarks. (a) Our proofs of Theorems 7 and 8 are based on the results for ladder variables. However, these theorems hold for *all* Lévy processes, the proofs being based on (i) discretizing the process Y into a (discrete time) random walk, (ii) using the corresponding results for this random walk, and then (iii) using separability arguments.

(b) In dealing with the process $Y(t) = X(t) - t$ of chapter 3 we first obtained what was essentially the transform of the joint distribution of $\{Y(t) - m(t), -m(t)\}$; from this we derived $v^*(s, \omega)$, which we used to obtain $E[e^{-sT_1 + i\omega Y(T_1)}]$ (Theorem 2, Lemma 4 and Theorem 9 of that chapter). Thus our knowledge of the special features of the net input process Y enabled us to reverse the arguments that we used in this section for processes of class $\mathscr{L}_+$.

5 The Insurance Risk Problem: General Case

We recall from section 4 of the preceding chapter that this problem is concerned with the random variable

$$T(x) = \inf\{t > 0 : x + \beta t - X(t) < 0\}, \tag{50}$$

where $x \geq 0$ and $X(t)$ is a compound Poisson process on $(-\infty, \infty)$ with zero drift. Let $Y(t) = X(t) - \beta t$. The results of section 1 show that $Y \in \mathscr{L}_+$ or $\mathscr{L}_-$ according as $\beta \geq 0$ or $\beta \leq 0$. It is seen that our problem reduces to the one concerning the supremum $M(t)$ of the process Y. We have the following:

Theorem 11. *For the random variable* (50) *we have*

$$1 + i\omega \int_0^\infty e^{i\omega x} E[e^{-sT(x)}]\, dx = \exp\left\{\int_0^\infty t^{-1} e^{-st} E[(e^{i\omega Y(t)} - 1);\, Y(t) > 0]\, dt\right\}$$

$$(s > 0,\ I_m(\omega) \geq 0). \tag{51}$$

PROOF. We have

$$P\{T(x) > t\} = P\{M(t) \leq x\}. \tag{52}$$

Now

$$i\omega s \int_0^\infty \int_0^\infty e^{i\omega x - st} P\{T(x) > t\}\, dt\, dx = i\omega s \int_0^\infty e^{i\omega x} \frac{1 - E[e^{-sT(x)}]}{s}\, dx$$

$$= -1 - i\omega \int_0^\infty e^{i\omega x} E[e^{-sT(x)}]\, dx$$

and

$$i\omega s \int_0^\infty \int_0^\infty e^{i\omega x - st} P\{M(t) \leq x\}\, dx\, dt = -s \int_0^\infty e^{-st} E[e^{i\omega M(t)}]\, dt.$$

Therefore (52) gives

$$1 + i\omega \int_0^\infty e^{i\omega x} E[e^{-sT(x)}]\, dx = s \int_0^\infty e^{-st} E[e^{i\omega M(t)}]\, dt$$

and (51) follows from Theorem 8. □

6 The Queue M/M/1

We consider the queueing system in which customers arrive in a Poisson process at a rate λ ($0 < \lambda < \infty$), and are served by a single server on a "first come, first served" basis, the service times of customers having the density $\mu e^{-\mu v}$ ($0 < \mu < \infty$). The mean inter-arrival time is λ^{-1} and the mean service time is μ^{-1}, so that the traffic intensity is $\rho = \lambda/\mu$. Let $Q(t)$ be the number of customers present in the system at time t (including the one being served, if any). We shall investigate the process $\{Q(t), t \geq 0\}$.

Let $A(t)$, $D(t)$ be two independent Poisson processes with parameters λ, μ respectively. The number of arrivals during a time interval $(0, t]$ is given by $A(t)$, while the number of departures is clearly equal to

$$\bar{D}(t) = \int_0^t 1_{Q(\tau-)>0}\, dD(\tau) \tag{53}$$

since the departures occur at a Poisson rate μ so long as the system is nonempty. Therefore

$$Q(t) = Q(0) + A(t) - \int_0^t 1_{Q(\tau-)>0}\, dD(\tau). \tag{54}$$

We can rewrite this as

$$Q(t) = Q(0) + Y(t) + \int_0^t 1_{Q(\tau-)=0}\, dD(\tau), \tag{55}$$

where $Y(t) = A(t) - D(t)$. We shall call $Y(t)$ the net input process; it is a compound Poisson process with zero drift. Its p.g.f. is given by

$$E[z^{Y(t)}] = E[z^{A(t)}]E[z^{-D(t)}] = e^{-vt[1 - C(z)]},$$

where $v = \lambda + \mu$ and $C(z) = pz + qz^{-1}$ with $vp = \lambda$, $vq = \mu$. Thus Y has been investigated in section 4.

The relation (55) is an integral equation for $Q(t)$. Our first concern is the existence and uniqueness of its solution. We have the following:

Theorem 12. *The integral equation* (55) *has the unique solution*

$$Q(t) = \max\{[Y(t) - Y(\tau-)](0 \leq \tau \leq t), Q(0) + Y(t)\}. \tag{56}$$

6 The Queue M/M/1

The proof of this theorem is along the same lines as that of Theorem 1 of chapter 3, and is therefore omitted. Actually the equation (55) yields much more information than concerning the queue length $Q(t)$. Thus, let us denote by T the busy period of the system with a given initial number $Q(0) = i > 0$ of customers. Thus

$$T = \inf\{t: Q(t) = 0\}. \tag{57}$$

In view of (55) we find that T has the same distribution as

$$T' = \inf\{t: Y(t) = -i\}, \tag{58}$$

which is the first passage time of the process Y from the origin to the state $-i < 0$. Therefore T' is identical with the ith descending ladder epoch $\bar{T}_i$ of Y, and Theorem 9 describes, in particular, the properties of the busy period initiated by a single customer. Furthermore, in view of (53) we may write the solution (56) as

$$Q(t) = Q(0) + A(t) - \bar{D}(t), \tag{59}$$

where

$$\bar{D}(t) = D(t) - \max\{0, -Q(0) - m(t)\} \tag{60}$$

with

$$m(t) = \inf_{0 \leq \tau \leq t} Y(\tau-) = \inf_{0 \leq \tau \leq t} Y(\tau) \quad \text{a.s.} \tag{61}$$

Here $\bar{D}(t)$ is the output of the system, namely, the number of departures during a time interval $(0, t]$. We shall investigate the bivariate process $\{Q(t), \bar{D}(t)\}$. It will be convenient to introduce the notation

$$I(t) = \int_0^t 1_{Q(\tau-)=0} \, dD(\tau). \tag{62}$$

Let $\tau_0 \equiv 0$, and τ_n $(n \geq 1)$ the epochs of successive jumps in the Poisson process $D(t)$. Then, writing

$$\chi(1) = 1_{Q(\tau-)=0}, \tag{63}$$

we find that

$$I(t) = \sum_{n=0}^{D(t)} \chi(\tau_n). \tag{64}$$

We have then the following.

Lemma 3. *For $z > 0$ we have*

$$z^{\sum_0^{D(t)} \chi(\tau_m)} = 1 - \left(\frac{1}{z} - 1\right) \sum_{n=0}^{D(t)} z^{\sum_0^n \chi(\tau_m)} \chi(\tau_n). \tag{65}$$

PROOF. We write

$$\left(\frac{1}{z}-1\right)\sum_{n=0}^{D(t)} z^{\sum_0^n \chi(\tau_m)} \chi(\tau_n) = \sum_{n=0}^{D(t)}\left[z^{\sum_0^n \chi(\tau_m)-1} - z^{\sum_0^n \chi(\tau_m)}\right]\chi(\tau_n)$$

$$= \sum_{n=0}^{D(t)}\left[z^{\sum_0^{n-1} \chi(\tau_m)} - z^{\sum_0^n \chi(\tau_m)}\right]\chi(\tau_n)$$

since we are concerned only with the terms for which $\chi(\tau_n) = 1$. A straightforward computation now yields the desired result. $\square$

Theorem 13. *For $s > 0$, $0 < z_1 < 1$, $z_2 > 0$ we have*

$$\int_0^\infty e^{-st} E[z_1^{Q(t)} z_2^{\bar{D}(t)} | Q(0) = i] \, dt = \frac{z_1^{i+1} - \mu(z_2 - z_1)J^*(z_2, s)}{(s + \lambda + \mu)z_1 - \lambda z_1^2 - \mu z_2}, \quad (66)$$

where $J^*(z, s) = \xi^{i+1}/\mu(z - \xi)$, $\xi \equiv \xi(z, s)$ being given by

$$\xi = \frac{s + \lambda + \mu - \sqrt{(s + \lambda + \mu)^2 - 4\lambda\mu z}}{2\lambda}. \quad (67)$$

PROOF. We have $\bar{D}(t) = D(t) - I(t)$, so

$$z_1^{Q(t)} z_2^{\bar{D}(t)} = z_1^{Q(0) + A(t) - D(t) + I(t)} z_2^{D(t) - I(t)}$$

$$= z_1^{Q(0) + A(t)} \left(\frac{z_2}{z_1}\right)^{D(t)} \left(\frac{z_2}{z_1}\right)^{-I(t)}$$

$$= z_1^{Q(0) + A(t)} \left(\frac{z_2}{z_1}\right)^{D(t)} \left[1 - \left(\frac{z_2}{z_1} - 1\right)\sum_{n=0}^{D(t)} \left(\frac{z_2}{z_1}\right)^{-\sum_0^n \chi(\tau_m)} \chi(\tau_n)\right]$$

by Lemma 3. Since $\chi(\tau_n) > 0$ iff $Q(\tau_n) = 0$, in which case

$$Q(0) + A(\tau_n) - D(\tau_n) + \sum_0^n \chi(\tau_m) = 0$$

from (55), we find that

$$z_1^{Q(t)} z_2^{\bar{D}(t)} = z_1^{Q(0) + A(t)} \left(\frac{z_2}{z_1}\right)^{D(t)}$$

$$- \left(\frac{z_2}{z_1} - 1\right) \sum_0^{D(t)} z_1^{A(t) - A(\tau_n)} \left(\frac{z_2}{z_1}\right)^{D(t) - D(\tau_n)} z_2^{Q(0) + A(\tau_n)} \chi(\tau_n)$$

$$= z_1^{Q(0) + A(t)} \left(\frac{z_2}{z_1}\right)^{D(t)}$$

$$- \left(\frac{z_2}{z_1} - 1\right) \int_0^t z_1^{A(t) - A(\tau)} \left(\frac{z_2}{z_1}\right)^{D(t) - D(\tau)} z_2^{Q(0) + A(\tau)} \chi(\tau) \, dD(\tau).$$

Using the fact that $A(\tau)$, $\chi(\tau)$ depend only on $Y(\tau')$ ($0 \le \tau' \le \tau$) and not on $A(t) - A(\tau)$, $D(t) - D(\tau)$, we obtain

$$E[z_1^{Q(t)} z_2^{\bar{D}(t)} | Q(0) = i] \quad (68)$$
$$= z_1^i e^{-t\phi(z_1, z_2)} - \left(\frac{z_2}{z_1} - 1\right) \int_0^t e^{-(t-\tau)\phi(z_1, z_2)} J(z_2, \tau) \mu \, d\tau,$$

where $J(z_2, t) = E[z_2^{i+A(t)}\chi(t)]$ and $\phi(z_1, z_2) = \lambda + \mu - \lambda z_1 - \mu z_2/z_1$. Let $J^*(z_2, s) = \int_0^\infty e^{-st} J(z_2, t)\, dt$. Then (68) leads to (66), where $J^*(z_2, s)$ can be evaluated as in the proof of Theorem 2 of chapter 3. □

Theorem 14. *For $s > 0$, $0 < z < 1$ we have*

$$\int_0^\infty e^{-st} E[z^{Q(t)} \mid Q(0) = i]\, dt = \frac{z^{i+1} - \mu(1-z)J^*(1, s)}{(s + \lambda + \mu)z - \lambda z^2 - \mu}. \tag{69}$$

Also, for $j \geq 0$

$$\lim_{t \to \infty} P\{Q(t) = j\} = 0 \qquad \text{if } \rho \geq 1 \tag{70}$$

$$= (1 - \rho)\rho^j \quad \text{if } \rho < 1.$$

PROOF. Putting $z_1 = z$, $z_2 = 1$ in (66) we obtain (69). To prove (70) we note that if $Q(0) = 0$, then (59)–(60) give $Q(t) = Y(t) - m(t) \sim M(t)$ by Lemma 1 of chapter 3, so $Q(t)$ converges in distribution. If $Q(0) \neq 0$ we proceed as in the proof of Theorem 4 of chapter 3 and find that $Q(t)$ converges in distribution in this case also. Recognizing $\xi(1, s)$ to be the root ξ of equation (38) we find that

$$\lim_{t \to \infty} E[z^{Q(t)} \mid Q(0) = i] = \lim_{s \to 0+} \frac{z^{i+1} - \mu(1-z)J^*(1, s)}{(s + \lambda + \mu)z - \lambda z^2 - \mu}$$

$$= 0 \qquad \text{if } \rho \geq 1,$$

$$= \frac{1 - \rho}{1 - \rho z} \quad \text{if } \rho < 1.$$

This leads to (70) and the proof is complete. □

The output $\bar{D}(t)$ is nondecreasing in t, and $\to \infty$ as $t \to \infty$, as can be verified from (66). However, we should be concerned with the properties of $D(t)$ as a process. In the case $\rho < 1$, if we take the initial queue length $Q(0)$ to be a random variable with the distribution $(1 - \rho)\rho^j$ $(j \geq 0)$, then it is known that (i) the output process is Poisson with parameter λ, and (ii) the queue length at time t is independent of the departure process in interval $(0, t]$. Theorem 15 (below) states a weaker result. In the cases $\rho \geq 1$, $Q(t)$ has limit distributions with appropriate location and scale parameters (Theorem 16).

Theorem 15. *Let $\rho < 1$ and $Q(0)$ have the distribution $(1 - \rho)\rho^j$ $(j \geq 0)$. Then $Q(t)$ and $\bar{D}(t)$ are independent and for $j \geq 0$*

$$P\{Q(t) = j\} = (1 - \rho)\rho^j, \qquad P\{\bar{D}(t) = j\} = e^{-\lambda t}\frac{(\lambda t)^j}{j!}. \tag{71}$$

PROOF. From Theorem 13 we obtain

$$\int_0^\infty e^{-st} E[z_1^{Q(t)} z_2^{\bar{D}(t)}] \, dt$$

$$= \left[\frac{(1-\rho)z_1}{1-\rho z_1} - \frac{(z_2 - z_1)}{(z_2 - \xi)} \cdot \frac{(1-\rho)\xi}{1-\xi\rho} \right] [(s + \lambda + \mu)z_1 - \lambda z_1^2 - \mu z_2]^{-1}.$$

After some simplification this last expression reduces to

$$\frac{1-\rho}{1-\rho z_1} \cdot \frac{1}{s + \lambda - \lambda z_2}.$$

Therefore

$$\int_0^\infty e^{-st} E[z_1^{Q(t)} z_2^{\bar{D}(t)}] \, dt = E[z_1^{Q(t)}] \int_0^\infty e^{-st} E[z_2^{\bar{D}(t)}] \, dt,$$

where

$$E[z_1^{Q(t)}] = \frac{1-\rho}{1-\rho z_1}, \qquad E[z_2^{\bar{D}(t)}] = e^{-\lambda t(1-z_2)}. \tag{72}$$

These p.g.f.'s lead to the desired results (71). □

Theorem 16. (i) *If $\rho > 1$, then*

$$\lim_{t \to \infty} P \left\{ \frac{Q(t) - (\lambda - \mu)t}{\sqrt{(\lambda + \mu)t}} < x \right\} = N(x). \tag{73}$$

(ii) *If $\rho = 1$, then*

$$\lim_{t \to \infty} P \left\{ \frac{Q(t)}{\sqrt{2\lambda t}} < x \right\} = N_+(x). \tag{74}$$

PROOF. Without loss of generality we assume $Q(0) = 0$. Then (59)–(60) give $Q(t) = Y(t) - m(t) \sim M(t)$ by Lemma 1 of chapter 3. The desired results now follow from (47)–(48). □

7 A Storage Model with Random Output

Let Y be the Lévy process

$$Y(t) = X_1(t) - X_2(t) - \beta t, \tag{75}$$

where X_1 is a compound Poisson process on $[0, \infty)$, X_2 a Lévy process with nondecreasing sample functions, and $\beta \geq 0$. (This process was considered in section 3.) Given this process and $x \geq 0$ we define a storage model in which the initial content is x and the net input during $(0, t]$ is $Y(t)$. This is done as follows. Let $t_0 \equiv 0$, t_n ($n \geq 1$) the epochs of successive

7 A Storage Model with Random Output   125

jumps in the process X_1, and $S_0 \equiv 0$, $S_n = Y(t_n-)$ $(n \geq 1)$. For the random walk $\{S_n, n \geq 0\}$ we define the random variables

$$\bar{N}_1 = \min\{n > 0: S_n \leq -x\},$$
$$\bar{N}_k = \min\{n > \bar{N}_{k-1}: S_n - S_{\bar{N}_{k-1}} \leq 0\} \quad (k \geq 2). \tag{76}$$

(If $x = 0$, these reduce to the descending ladder epochs of $\{S_n\}$.) Also, let $\bar{T}_0 \equiv 0$, $\bar{T}_k = t_{\bar{N}_k}$ $(k \geq 1)$. The storage process $\{Z(t), t \geq 0\}$ is defined as follows:

$$Z(t) = \max\{0, x + Y(t)\} \quad \text{for } 0 \leq t < \bar{T}_1,$$
$$= \max\{0, Y(t) - Y(\bar{T}_{\bar{N}}-)\} \quad \text{for } t \geq \bar{T}_1, \tag{77}$$

where $\bar{N} \equiv \bar{N}(t) = \max\{k: \bar{T}_k \leq t\}$. Here $\bar{T}_1 > 0$, $\bar{T}_k - \bar{T}_{k-1} > 0$ $(k \geq 2)$ a.s., so that $\bar{T}_k \to \infty$ as $k \to \infty$ and therefore the process $Z(t)$ is well defined. The above definition of $Z(t)$ leads to an explicit expression for $Z(t)$ given by the following:

Theorem 17. *For the storage process* $\{Z(t), t \geq 0\}$ *defined by* (77) *we have*

$$Z(t) = \max\{Y(t) - m(t), x + Y(t)\}, \tag{78}$$

where $m(t)$ *is the infimum of the process* Y.

PROOF. Let $\tau = \inf\{t: Y(t) \leq -x\}$. Then $0 \leq \tau < \bar{T}_1$ and

$$m(t) > -x \quad \text{for } 0 \leq t < \tau,$$
$$= Y(t) \quad \text{for } \tau \leq t < \bar{T}_1.$$

Therefore the right side of (78) becomes $\max\{0, x + Y(t)\} = Z(t)$ for $0 \leq t < \bar{T}_1$ by (77).

Next let $\bar{N} > 0$. Then since $\{Y(\bar{T}_k-)\}$ is a nonincreasing sequence, $m(t) = \min\{Y(\bar{T}_{\bar{N}}-), Y(t)\}$ and the right side of (78) becomes

$$\max\{Y(t) - \min[Y(\bar{T}_{\bar{N}}-), Y(t)], x + Y(t)\}$$
$$= \max\{0, Y(t) - Y(\bar{T}_{\bar{N}}-), x + Y(t)\} = \max\{0, Y(t) - Y(\bar{T}_{\bar{N}}-)\}$$

since $Y(t) \leq -x$ for $\bar{N} > 0$. Thus (78) is true for all $t \geq 0$ and the theorem is completely proved. □

For $x = 0$ Theorem 17 gives $Z(t) = Y(t) - m(t) \sim M(t)$ and the distribution of $Z(t)$ follows from Theorem 8. For $x \geq 0$ we have the following:

Theorem 18. *For* $I_m(\omega) \geq 0$, $I_m(\omega_1) < 0$ *we have*

$$\int_0^\infty i\omega_1 e^{-i\omega_1 x} \int_0^\infty e^{-st}E[e^{i\omega Z(t)} | Z(0) = x] \, dt \, dx \tag{79}$$

$$= \frac{u^*(s, \omega)}{su^*(s, 0)} + \frac{\omega}{\omega_1 - \omega} u^*(s, \omega)v^*(s, \omega_1).$$

PROOF. Proceeding as in the proof of Lemma 1 of chapter 3 we find that $\{Y(t) - m(t), Y(t)\} \sim \{M(t), Y(t)\}$. Therefore

$$P\{Z(t) \leq y \,|\, Z(0) = x\}$$
$$= P\{M(t) \leq y, x + Y(t) \leq y\}$$
$$= \sum_{k=0}^{\infty} P\{M(t) \leq y, x + Y(t) \leq y, T_k \leq t < T_{k+1}\}$$
$$= \sum_{k=0}^{\infty} \int_0^t \int_0^y P\{T_k \in d\tau, Y(T_k) \in dz\}$$
$$\quad \times P\{x + Y(t) \leq y, T_{k+1} > t \,|\, T_k = \tau, Y(T_k) = z\}$$
$$= \int_0^t \int_0^y u(d\tau, dz) P\{Y(t-\tau) \leq y - x - z, T_1 > t - \tau\}.$$

This gives

$$P\{Z(t) \in dy \,|\, Z(0) = x\}$$
$$= \int_0^t u(d\tau, dy) P\{Y(t-\tau) \leq -x, T_1 > t - \tau\}$$
$$+ \int_0^t \int_0^y u(d\tau, dz) P\{Y(t-\tau) \in dy - x - z, T_1 > t - \tau\}.$$

Here $u(t, y) = \sum_0^\infty P\{T_k \leq t, Y(T_k) \leq y\}$. The desired transform is

$$\int_0^\infty e^{-st} E[e^{i\omega Z(t)} \,|\, Z(0) = x] \, dt$$
$$= \int_0^\infty \int_0^\infty e^{-s\tau + i\omega y} u(d\tau, dy) \int_0^\infty e^{-st} P\{Y(t) \leq -x, T_1 > t\} \, dt \qquad (80)$$
$$+ \int_0^\infty \int_0^\infty e^{-s\tau + i\omega z} u(d\tau, dz) \int_0^\infty \int_{-x}^0 e^{-st + i\omega(x+y)} P\{Y(t) \in dy, T_1 > t\} \, dt$$
$$= \frac{u^*(s, \omega)}{su^*(s, 0)} + u^*(s, \omega)[v_x^*(s, \omega) - v_x^*(s, 0)],$$

where

$$v_x^*(s, \omega) = \int_0^\infty e^{-st} E[e^{i\omega[x + Y(t)]}; x + Y(t) \geq 0, T_1 > t] \, dt. \qquad (81)$$

It can be easily verified that

$$\int_0^\infty i\omega_1 e^{i\omega_1 x} v_x^*(s, \omega) \, dx = \frac{\omega_1}{\omega_1 - \omega} v^*(s, \omega_1). \qquad (82)$$

The theorem follows from (80)–(82). It should be noted that when $x = 0$ $v_x^*(s, \omega) = v_x^*(s, 0)$ and in the last expression in (80) the first reduces to

$$\int_0^\infty e^{-st} E[e^{i\omega M(t)}] \, dt$$

in view of Theorem 8. □

The random variable τ defined in the proof of Theorem 17 is clearly the busy (wet) period of our storage model with the initial content $Z(0) = x$. The idle (dry) period that follows this busy period is given by $\bar{T}_1 - \tau$. Since $\bar{T}_1 - \tau$ is independent of τ and has density $\lambda e^{-\lambda t}$, it follows that

$$E[e^{-s\bar{T}_1} | Z(0) = x] = \frac{\lambda}{s + \lambda} E[e^{-s\tau} | Z(0) = x]. \tag{83}$$

It remains to evaluate the transform on the left side of (83). However, we shall evaluate the transform of $\bar{T}_1$ when $Z(0)$ is identified as the first jump in X_1, that is, $Z(0)$ is a random variable with the d.f. B. [Here λ and B are the jump rate and jump size d.f. of the compound Poisson process X_1.] We have the following:

Theorem 19. *Let $Z(0)$ have d.f. B. Then for $s > 0$*

$$E[e^{-s\bar{T}_1}] = 1 - \frac{s}{s + \lambda} \exp\left\{\int_0^\infty t^{-1} e^{-st} P\{Y(t) > 0\} \, dt\right\}. \tag{84}$$

PROOF. Let $\tilde{Y}(t) = x + Y(t) - J(t)$, where $J(t)$ is the last jump in X_1 before t. Then $\tilde{Y}(t_n) = x + Y(t_n-)$ with probability one. If x has d.f. B, then $\tilde{Y}(t)$ and $Y(t)$ have the same finite dimensional distributions. Therefore the $\bar{N}_k$ have the same distribution as the (descending) ladder variables of the random walk $\{Y(t_n), n \geq 0\}$. Recall that $\bar{T}_1 = t_{\bar{N}_1}$. For the random walk $\{(t_n, Y(t_n)\}$ we have already obtained the distribution of the ascending ladder epoch T_1 in Theorem 6. The Wiener–Hopf factorization then gives

$$1 - E(e^{-st_1}) = [1 - E(e^{-sT_1})][1 - E(e^{-s\bar{T}_1})], \tag{85}$$

where

$$E(e^{-st_1}) = \frac{\lambda}{s + \lambda}, \tag{86}$$

and by Theorem 6,

$$1 - E(e^{-sT_1}) = \exp\left\{-\int_0^\infty t^{-1} e^{-st} P\{Y(t) > 0\} \, dt\right\}. \tag{87}$$

The desired result follows from (85)–(87). □

8 Further Remarks

(a) Storage Models of Chapter 3

For references prior to 1965 to the literature on the models of chapter 3, see Prabhu (1965). The storage model of section 8 was proposed by Hasofer [(1966a), (1966b)], who assumed the input to be compound Poisson. The waiting time process in the G/M/1 system (section 9) was investigated by Prabhu [(1964), (1970a)]. The analysis of the static priority system is due to Hooke and Prabhu (1971). The analysis of the dynamic priority system is due to Goldberg (1977).

(b) Ladder Processes

Ladder processes arising from Lévy processes were investigated by Prabhu (1970b) in the special case of $Y(t) = X(t) - t$ where X is a Lévy process on $[0, \infty)$. This is the net input process of the storage models investigated in chapter 3. [See also Prabhu and Rubinovitch (1970).] A systematic theory of ladder phenomena in Lévy processes was developed by Rubinovitch (1971) using J. F. C. Kingman's theory of regenerative phenomena [see Kingman (1972)]. Further work was done by Prabhu and Rubinovitch [(1971), (1973)].

(c) Wiener–Hopf Factorization

As already remarked in section 1 of chapter 4, a Wiener–Hopf factorization completely analogous to the one for random walks (that is, in terms of the ladder epochs T, $\bar{T}$) holds iff Y is a compound Poisson with zero drift. However, for arbitrary Lévy processes Y, Rogozin (1966) obtained the identity

$$\frac{s}{s + \phi(\omega)} = r_+(s, \omega) r_-(s, \omega) \qquad (s > 0, \omega \text{ real}), \tag{88}$$

where

$$r_+(s, \omega) = \exp\left\{\int_0^\infty (e^{i\omega x} - 1) v_s(dx)\right\}, \tag{89}$$

$$r_-(s, \omega) = \exp\left\{\int_{-\infty}^0 (e^{i\omega x} - 1) v_s(dx)\right\}. \tag{90}$$

It should be noted that for fixed $s > 0$, $r_+(s, \omega)$ and $r_-(s, \omega)$ are c.f.'s of infinitely divisible distributions concentrated on $(0, \infty)$ and $(-\infty, 0)$ respectively. Among such factors this factorization is unique up to a factor $e^{ia\omega}$, a being a real function of s.

In the case where $Y \in \mathscr{L}_+ \cup \mathscr{L}_-$ the factorization (88) says something more, namely it identifies the factors in terms of ladder epochs. Thus if $Y \in \mathscr{L}_+$ we find from Lemma 1 that

$$r_+(s, \omega) = \frac{u^*(s, \omega)}{u^*(s, 0)}, \qquad r_-(s, \omega) = \frac{v^*(s, \omega)}{v^*(s, 0)}, \qquad (91)$$

where $u^*(s, \omega)$ and $v^*(s, \omega)$ are defined by (26) and (27), in terms of the ascending ladder epoch T.

The most significant result in this area is due to Fristedt (1974). Let M and m be the supremum and infimum functions of Y. Let $L(t)$ be the local time of the process $M - X$ at zero (unique up to a multiplicative constant), $T_+(\tau)$ its inverse and $Z_+(\tau)$ the process $\{T_+(\tau), M(T_+(\tau))\}$. Then Z_+ is a subordinator in R^2 and

$$E[e^{-sT_+(\tau) + i\omega M(T_+(\tau))}] = e^{-\tau \phi_+(s, \omega)}, \qquad (92)$$

where

$$\phi_+(s, \omega) = c_+ \exp\left\{\int_0^\infty \int_0^\infty (e^{-t} - e^{-st + i\omega x}) t^{-1} F(t, dx) \, dt\right\}. \qquad (93)$$

Let $\phi_-(s, \omega)$ be obtained in a similar way using $m(t)$ instead of $M(t)$, so that

$$\phi_-(s, \omega) = c_- \exp\left\{\int_0^\infty \int_{-\infty}^0 (e^{-t} - e^{-st + i\omega x}) t^{-1} F(t, dx) \, dt\right\}. \qquad (94)$$

It is easily verified that

$$s + \phi(\omega) = \phi_+(s, \omega) \phi_-(s, \omega) \qquad (s > 0, \omega \text{ real}). \qquad (95)$$

All the results described above are concerned with the factorization of the function $s + \phi(\omega)$. Prabhu (1972) established the factorization as a property of the semigroup of convolution operators associated with the Lévy process Y. See also Greenwood (1973) and Prabhu (1976).

(d) Renewal-Reward Processes

For the two-dimensional random walk of section 2, let $N(t) = \max\{n: S_n \leq t\}$ and

$$\begin{aligned} X(t) &= 0 &&\text{if } N(t) = 0 \\ &= \sum_1^{N(t)} X_k &&\text{if } N(t) > 0. \end{aligned} \qquad (96)$$

Jewell (1967) who introduced this random walk calls X a renewal-reward process. The ascending and descending ladder epochs of X are given by

$T = T_N$ and $\bar{T} = T_{\bar{N}}$ respectively. It turns out that for this non-Markovian process there exists a Wiener–Hopf factorization [see problem 3]. If τ_k, X_k are independent and τ_k has exponential density, then $X(t)$ reduces to a compound Poisson process.

(e) Insurance Risk

The solution of the insurance risk problem in the general case is due to H. Cramér who derived the integro-differential equation satisfied by $F(t, x) = P\{T(x) > t\}$ (see problem 13 of the Introduction), and applied Wiener–Hopf techniques to solve it. Specifically, he used the identity

$$\frac{s + \phi(\omega)}{s + \lambda + i\omega\beta} = \frac{B(s, \omega)}{A(s, \omega)} \quad (s > 0, \omega \text{ real}), \tag{97}$$

where

$$A(s, \omega) = \exp\left\{\int_0^\infty t^{-1} e^{-st} E[e^{i\omega Y(t)}; Y(t) > 0, N(t) > 0] \, dt\right\} \tag{98}$$
$$(s > 0, I_m(\omega) \geq 0),$$

$$B(s, \omega) = \exp\left\{-\int_0^\infty t^{-1} e^{-st} E[e^{i\omega Y(t)}; Y(t) \leq 0, N(t) > 0] \, dt\right\} \tag{99}$$
$$(s > 0, I_m(\omega) \leq 0),$$

λ is the jump rate of X and $N(t)$ is the number of jumps in X during $(0, t]$. See problem 2. Cramér's work is a pioneering contribution whose significance goes beyond insurance risk theory. It turns out that the factorization (97) for the compound Poisson process is the earliest result in the area of Wiener–Hopf factorization for Lévy processes, being a special case of Rogozin's result (88). [See Prabhu (1973).] When $\beta = 0$, (97) reduces to (10).

(f) The Queue M/M/1

The integral equation (54) for $Q(t)$ was used by Martins-Neto and Wong (1976) to formulate a control problem. Note that

$$M(t) = A(t) - \lambda t, \quad m(t) = D(t) - \mu t \tag{100}$$

are both martingales and (54) can be written in terms of M and m.

(g) Storage Models with Random Output

The storage model of section 7 was first investigated by Gani and Pyke (1960). Later, Grinstein and Rubinovitch (1974) formulated essentially the same model for a queueing system with Poisson arrivals and service mechanism such that the amount of work done by the server during a time interval $(0, t]$ is represented by a Lévy process $X_2(t)$ assuming customers to be present throughout $(0, t]$.

Problems

1. If the jump size distribution is K, and N, $\bar{N}$ are the ascending strong and descending weak ladder epochs of the random walk induced by K, show that the factorization (10) may be written as

$$1 - z\psi(\omega) = [1 - E(z^N e^{i\omega S_N})][1 - E[z^{\bar{N}} e^{i\omega S_{\bar{N}}})], \tag{101}$$

where $\psi(\omega)$ is the c.f. of K and $z = v(v + s)^{-1}$, v being the jump rate.

2. Let Y be a Lévy process of the type $Y(t) = X_1(t) - X_2(t) - \beta t$, where X_1 is a compound Poisson process on $(-\infty, \infty)$, X_2 a Lévy process with nondecreasing sample functions, independent of X_1, and β is a real number. Let

$$\chi(s, \omega) = 1 - \exp\left\{-\int_0^\infty t^{-1} e^{-st} E[e^{i\omega Y(t)}; Y(t) > 0, N(t) > 0] \, dt\right\} \tag{102}$$

$$(s > 0, I_m(\omega) \geq 0)$$

and

$$\bar{\chi}(s, \omega) = 1 - \exp\left\{-\int_0^\infty t^{-1} e^{-st} E[e^{i\omega Y(t)}; Y(t) \leq 0, N(t) > 0] \, dt\right\} \tag{103}$$

$$(s > 0, I_m(\omega) \leq 0).$$

Establish the Wiener–Hopf factorization

$$\frac{s + \phi(\omega)}{s + \lambda + i\omega\beta + \phi_2(-\omega)} = [1 - \chi(s, \omega)][1 - \bar{\chi}(s, \omega)] \quad (s > 0, \omega \text{ real}), \tag{104}$$

where λ is the jump rate of X_1, $N(t)$ is the number of jumps in X_1 during $(0, t]$,

$$E[e^{i\omega Y(t)}] = e^{-t\phi(\omega)}, \quad \text{and} \quad E[e^{i\omega X_2(t)}] = e^{-t\phi_2(\omega)}. \tag{105}$$

When $X_2 \equiv 0$, (104) reduces to Cramér's factorization (97).

3. For the renewal-reward process $X(t)$ defined by (96), show that

$$s \int_0^\infty e^{-st} E[e^{i\omega X(t)}] \, dt = r_+(s, \omega) r_-(s, \omega), \tag{106}$$

where

$$r_+(s, \omega) = \exp\left\{\int_0^\infty (e^{i\omega x} - 1)v_s(dx)\right\}, \quad (107)$$

$$r_-(s, \omega) = \exp\left\{\int_{-\infty}^0 (e^{i\omega x} - 1)v_a(dx)\right\}, \quad (108)$$

and v_s is the Lévy measure given by

$$v_s\{0\} = 0, \ v_s(dx) = \sum_1^\infty \frac{1}{n}\int_0^\infty e^{-st}F_n(dt, dx) \quad (x \neq 0), \quad (109)$$

$F_n(t, x)$ being the d.f. of (T_n, S_n). [When $X(t)$ reduces to the compound Poisson with zero drift, (106) reduces to Rogozin's identity (88).]

4. For the queue M/M/1 prove the following:

(i) The distribution of the net input process $Y(t)$ is given by

$$k_j(t) = P\{Y(t) = j\} = e^{-(\lambda+\mu)t}\rho^{j/2}I_j(2\sqrt{\lambda\mu}\,t) \quad (j = \ldots, -1, 0, 1, 2, \ldots), \quad (110)$$

where I_j is the modified Bessel function of index j, defined as

$$I_j(x) = \sum_{n=0}^\infty \frac{(x/2)^{2n+j}}{n!\,(n+j)!}. \quad (111)$$

(ii) The Laplace transform of $k_j(t)$ is given by

$$\int_0^\infty e^{-st}k_j(t)\,dt = \frac{\eta^{-j}}{\lambda(\eta - \xi)} \quad \text{for } j \geq 0,$$

$$= \frac{\xi^{-j}}{\lambda(\eta - \xi)} \quad \text{for } j \leq 0, \quad (112)$$

where ξ, η are given by (39)–(40).

(iii)

$$P\{Q(t) < j \mid Q(0) = i\} = K_{j-i}(t) - \rho^j K_{-j-i}(t), \quad (113)$$

where

$$K_j(t) = \sum_{-\infty}^{j-1} k_\nu(t). \quad (114)$$

5. In the storage model of section 7, let

$$\tau_1 = \inf\{t: Y(t) \leq -x\},$$

$$\tau_k = \inf\{t: Y(t) - Y(\overline{T}_{k-1}-) \leq 0\} \quad (k \geq 2). \quad (115)$$

Then $\tau_k < \overline{T}_k$ a.s. Let $I_k = \overline{T}_k - \tau_k$ $(k \geq 1)$, so that I_k is the kth dry period. The total dry period during $(0, t]$ is given by

$$I(t) = I_1 + I_2 + \cdots + I_{\overline{N}} \quad \text{for } \overline{T}_{\overline{N}} \leq t < \tau_{N+1},$$

$$= I_1 + I_2 + \cdots + I_{\overline{N}} + (t - \tau_{\overline{N}+1}) \quad \text{for } \tau_{N+1} \leq t < \overline{T}_{\overline{N}+1}, \quad (116)$$

for $\overline{N} \equiv \overline{N}(t) \geq 0$. Here $I_1, I_2, \ldots$ are independent random variables with density $\lambda e^{-\lambda t}$. In the case $X_2 \equiv 0, \beta = 1$, show that

$$I(t) = \max\{0, -x - m(t)\}. \quad (117)$$

6. Continuation. Using Theorem 19 show that $\overline{T}_1$ is a proper random variable iff

$$A = \int_0^\infty t^{-1} P\{Y(t) < 0, N_1(t) > 0\}\, dt = \infty, \tag{118}$$

where $N_1(t)$ is the number of jumps in X_1 during $(0, t]$. In this case

$$E(\overline{T}_1) = \lambda^{-1} \exp\left\{\int_0^\infty t^{-1} P\{Y(t) > 0\}\, dt\right\} \leq \infty. \tag{119}$$

References

Fristedt, Bert (1974): Sample functions of stochastic processes with stationary independent increments. *Advances in Probability* 3, Marcel Dekker, New York.

Gani, J. and Pyke, R. (1960): The content of a dam as the supremum of an infinitely divisible process. *J. Math. and Mech.* 9, 639–652.

Goldberg, H. M. (1977): Analysis of the earliest due date scheduling rule in queueing systems. *Math. Opns. Res.* 2, 145–154.

Grinstein, J. and Rubinovitch (1974): Queues with random service output: the case of Poisson arrivals. *J. Appl. Prob.* 11, 771–784.

Greenwood, P. (1973): On Prabhu's factorization of Lévy generators. *Z. Wahrscheinlichkeitstheorie verw. Geb.* 27, 75–77.

Hasofer, A. M. (1966a): The almost full dam with Poisson input. *J. Roy. Statist. Soc. B* 28, 329–335.

Hasofer, A. M. (1966b): The almost full dam with Poisson input: further results. *J. Roy. Statist. Soc. B* 28, 448–455.

Hooke, J. A. and Prabhu, N. U. (1971): Priority queues in heavy traffic. *Opsearch* 8, 1–9.

Jewell, W. S. (1967): Fluctuations of a renewal-reward process. *J. Math. Anal. Appl.* 19, 309–329.

Kingman, J. F. C. (1972): *Regenerative Phenomena*. John Wiley, New York.

Martins-Neto, A. F. and Wong, E. (1976): A martingale approach to queues. *Stochastic Systems: Modeling, Identification and Optimization I* (Rogers J.-B. Wets, ed.). North-Holland Publishing Company, Amsterdam.

Prabhu, N. U. (1964): A waiting time process in the queue GI/M/1. *Acta. Math. Acad. Sci. Hung.* 15, 363–371.

Prabhu, N. U. (1965): *Queues and Inventories*. John Wiley, New York.

Prabhu, N. U. (1970a): The queue GI/M/1 with traffic intensity one. *Studia Sci. Math. Hungar.* 5, 89–96.

Prabhu, N. U. (1970b): Ladder variables for a continuous time stochastic process. *Z. Wahrscheinlichketistheorie verw. Geb.* 16, 157–164.

Prabhu, N. U. (1972): Wiener–Hopf factorization for convolution semigroups. *Z. Wahrscheinlichkeitstheorie verw. Geb.* 23, 103–113.

Prabhu, N. U. (1973): Recent research on the ruin problem of collective risk theory. *Inventory Control and Water Storage* (A. Prekopa, ed.). North-Holland Publishing Company, Amsterdam.

Prabhu, N. U. (1976): Ladder sets and regenerative phenomena: further remarks and some applications. *Sankhya* **38A**, 143–152.

Prabhu, N. U. and Rubinovitch, M. (1970): A regenerative phenomenon occurring in a storage model. *J. Roy. Statist. Soc. B* **32**, 354–361.

Prabhu, N. U. and Rubinovitch, M. (1971): On a continuous time extension of Feller's lemma. *Z. Wahrscheinlichkeitstheorie verw. Geb.* **17**, 220–226.

Prabhu, N. U. and Rubinovitch, M. (1973): Further results for ladder processes in continuous time. *Stochastic Processes Appl.* **1**, 151–168.

Rogozin, B. A. (1966): On the distribution of functions related to boundary problems for processes with independent increments. *Theor. Probab. Appl.* **11**, 580–591.

Rubinovitch, M. (1971): Ladder phenomena in stochastic processes with stationary independent increments. *Z. Wahrscheinlichkeitstheorie verw. Geb.* **20**, 58–74.

Appendix

Theorem A1. Let $K(z) = k_0 + k_1 z + k_2 z^2 + \cdots$ be a p.g.f. with $k_0 > 0$ and $0 < K'(1) = \alpha$. Then the equation

$$\xi = zK(\xi) \tag{1}$$

has a unique continuous root $\xi \equiv \xi(z)$ in $(0, 1)$ such that $\xi(0+) = 0$. Also, as $z \to 1-$, $\xi(z)$ converges to the least positive root ζ of the equation $\zeta = K(\zeta)$, and $0 < \zeta < 1$ iff $\alpha > 1$.

PROOF. Consider the function

$$f(x) = \frac{K(x)}{x} = \frac{k_0}{x} + k_1 + k_2 x + k_3 x^2 + \cdots \qquad (0 < x < 1).$$

We have $f(0+) = \infty$, $f(1-) = 1$. Moreover,

$$f''(x) = \frac{2k_0}{x^3} + 2k_3 + 6k_4 x + \cdots \quad > 0.$$

It follows that $f(x)$ is monotone decreasing and > 1 for $x < \zeta$ where ζ is the least positive root of the equation $f(x) = 1$, and $\zeta < 1$ or $= 1$ depending on whether $f'(1) = \alpha - 1 > 0$ or ≤ 0. Therefore for a given z in $(0, 1)$ there is a unique x such that $f(x) = z^{-1}$ in the range $(0 < x < \zeta)$ and from (1) it is clear that $x = \xi(z)$. Clearly ξ is a continuous function of z and $\to 0$ as $z \to 0+$. Also $z \to 1-$, $\xi(z) \to \zeta$.

Theorem A2. Let $\psi(\theta)$ be the Laplace transform of a distribution $(\theta > 0)$ and $\rho = -\lambda \psi'(0)/k$ where $0 < \lambda < \infty$ and k is a positive integer. Then for $0 < z < 1$ the equation

$$\gamma^k = z\psi(\theta + \lambda - \lambda\gamma) \tag{2}$$

has exactly k distinct roots $\gamma_r \equiv \gamma_r(z, \theta)$ with $|\gamma_r| < 1$ ($r = 1, 2, \ldots k$). As $z \to 1-$ and $\theta \to 0+$, $\gamma_r(z, \theta) \to \zeta_r$ where ζ_r are the roots of the equation

$$\zeta^k = z\psi(\lambda - \lambda\zeta) \qquad (3)$$

with $|\zeta_r| < 1$ ($r = 1, 2, \ldots, k$) if $\rho > 1$, while $|\zeta_r| < 1$ ($r = 1, 2, \ldots, k-1$) and $\zeta_k = 1$ if $\rho \le 1$.

PROOF. Let $|x| = 1 - \varepsilon$ for ε sufficiently small and positive.

Then
$$|z\psi(\theta + \lambda - \lambda x)| < (1 - \varepsilon)^k$$

and by Rouche's theorem the equation $x^k = z\psi(\theta + \lambda - \lambda x)$ has exactly k roots with $|x| < 1 - \varepsilon$. The remaining results follow from continuity arguments.

Theorem A3. *Let* $\phi(\theta) = \int_0^\infty (1 - e^{-\theta x})v(dx)$ ($\theta > 0$), *where* v *is a Lévy measure, and* $\rho = \int_0^\infty xv(dx)$. *Then for* $s > 0$ *the equation*

$$\eta = s + \phi(\eta) \qquad (4)$$

has a unique continuous solution $\eta \equiv \eta(s)$ *with* $\eta(\infty) = \infty$. *Furthermore*:

(i) *as* $s \to 0+$, $\eta(s) \to \eta_0$ *is the largest positive root of the equation* $\eta_0 = \phi(\eta_0)$, *and* $\eta_0 > 0$ *iff* $\rho > 1$;
(ii) $\eta'(0+) = (1 - \rho)^{-1}$ *if* $\rho < 1$, *and* $= \infty$ *if* $\rho = 1$.

PROOF. Consider the function $f(x) = x - \phi(x)$ ($x > 0$). We have $f(0+) = 0$, $f(\infty) = \infty$ and

$$f''(x) = \int_0^\infty y^2 e^{-xy}v(dy) > 0.$$

It follows that $f(x)$ is positive and monotone increasing for $x > \eta_0$, where η_0 is the largest positive root of $f(x) = 0$, and $\eta_0 = 0$ or > 0 depending on whether $f'(0) = 1 - \rho \ge 0$ or < 0. Thus for a given $s > 0$, there is a unique x such that $f(x) = s$ in the range $x > \eta_0$ and it is clear from (4) that $x = \eta(s)$. It is clear that $\eta(s)$ is a continuous function of s and $\to \infty$ as $s \to \infty$. Also, as $s \to 0+$, $\eta(s) \to \eta_0$, which proves (i). The remaining result follows easily.

Index

Andersen, Sparre E. 63
Arrow, K.J., Karlin, S., and Scarf, H. 9

Barrois, T. 9
Baxter, G. 44, 63
Beard, R.E., Pentikäinen, T., and Personen, E. 14
Beekman, J.A. 14
Beneš, V.E. 13, 38, 64
Bessel function 132
Blackwell, D. 43, 64
Brownian motion 70, 71, 109
Buhlmann, H. 15
Busy cycle 53
Busy period 20
   in priority systems 107
Busy period transitions 45

Canonical measure 70
Characteristic function xi
Cohen, J.W. 13
Completion time 107
Control 6
Convolution operators 129
Cramér, H. 9, 53, 130, 131

Dam model of a 4
  , continuous time 71, 81
  , discrete time 4
  , finite capacity 4, 92
  , infinite capacity 12
  , infinitely deep 12, 92
Design 6
Directly Riemann-integrable 98
Distribution function xi
Dormoy, E. 9
Drift
  of a random walk 22, 23
  of a Lévy process 71, 109
Duality 31, 94

$E_k/G/1$
  busy period 61
  idle period 61
  waiting time 61
  Wiener–Hopf factorization 59
Erdös, P. and Kac, M. 30, 64

Feller, W. 29, 43, 49, 64
First passage time 79
Fluctuation theory
  of Lévy processes 7

137

Fluctuation theory *(cont.)*
   of random walks 7, 111
   Fristedt, B. 129, 133
$G/E_k/1$
   busy period 60
   idle period 60
   ladder points 59
   waiting time 60
$G/G/1$
   busy cycle 53
   busy period 20, 53, 56
   idle period 2, 19, 53, 56
   ladder points 21, 53
   waiting time 1, 19, 27
$G/M/1$
   busy cycle 97
   busy period 36, 57
   idle period 36, 57
   ladder points 35
   queue-length 39, 42
   waiting time 36, 95, 98
   Wiener–Hopf factorization 35
Gamma density 72, 105
Gani, J. and Pyke, R. 65, 131, 133
Gnedenko, B.V. and Kovalenko, I.N. 13
Goldberg, H.M. 128, 133
Grand Coulee Dam 9
Greenwood, P. 129
Grinstein, J. and Rubinovitch, M. 131, 133

Hasofer, A.M. 128, 133
Heyde, C.C. 28, 64
Hitting times 7
Holdaway, H.W. 9
Hooke, J.A. and Prabhu, N.U. 128, 133
Hurst, H.E. 9, 14

Idle period 2, 19
Input into a dam 4, 71
   $M/G/1$ 68
   $M/M/1$ 132
   storage systems 105, 108, 128
Insurance risk 5, 13, 68, 85, 108, 119, 130
   , general case for 119
   , negative process for 85
   , positive process for 86
Integral equations 8, 75, 100, 120
Integro-differential equation 130
Inventory models
   of (s,S) type 3
   with continuous time 5
   with backlog allowed 3
   with no backlog 3
Inverse Gaussian
   density 83
   process 105

Jaiswal, N.K. 14
Jewell, W.S. 129, 133

Kemperman, J.H.B. 44, 64
Kendall, D.G. 8, 14, 38, 64
Kingman, J.F.C. 128, 133
Kleinrock, L. 14
Koopmans, T.C. 9, 14
Krein, M.G. 44, 64

Ladder points
   in a compound Poisson process 117
   in a Lévy process 86, 110, 114, 128
   in a random walk 21, 43, 48, 111
Laplace transform xi
Lévy measure 51, 72, 82
Lévy processes 7, 8, 65, 69, 72, 73, 83, 90, 108, 112, 114, 118
   of supremum and infimum 74, 77, 113, 129
   with bounded variation 71, 109
Lifetime of a process 84
Lindley, D.V. 17, 44, 64
Little, J.D.C. 9, 14
Long run cost 7
Lundberg, F. 9

$M/G/1$ 8, 37
   balking 80
   batch arrivals 80
   busy period 37, 79, 80
   idle period 37

ladder points 40
modified service rule 80
queue-length 38, 41
waiting time 37
M/M/1
  busy period 33
  idle period 33
  ladder points 32
  queue-length 2, 120
  waiting time 33
  Wiener–Hopf factorization 32
Markov
  chain 45
  process 7, 8, 91, 109
Martingales 130
Martins-Neto, A.F. and Wong, E. 130, 133
Massé, P. 9, 14
Maximum and minimum 7
Monotone ordering policy 4
Moran, P.A.P. 9, 12, 14, 655

Net risk premium 68
Normal distribution xi

One-sided normal distribution 11
Optimization 7
Ordering policies 3
Output from a dam 4
  M/M/1 121, 123
Overflow 4, 12, 92, 106

Partial lack of memory 35, 57
Period of prosperity 85
Poisson process
  , compound 5, 52, 68, 69, 71, 84, 96, 99, 110, 112, 116, 119, 124, 128
  , simple 2, 67, 108, 120
Pollaczek–Khintchine formula 38
Prabhu, N.U. 9, 14, 46, 64, 128, 129, 130, 133, 134
Prabhu, N.U. and Rubinovitch, M. 128, 134
Priorities
  , dynamic 8, 99
  , head-of-the-line 8, 99

, pre-emptive repeat 8
, pre-emptive resume 8, 99
, static 8, 99
Probability generating function xi

Queue-discipline
  earliest due date 103
  , first come, first served 1, 8
  , last come, first served 80
  priorities 8
Queue-length 2, 6
Queueing system
  , $E_k/G/1$ 61
  , $G/E_k/1$ 58
  , $G/G/1$ 8, 53
  , $G/M/1$ 8, 34, 45, 56, 95, 96, 98, 107, 128
  , $M/G/1$ 8, 34, 56, 67, 73, 74, 83, 105
  , $M/M/1$ 8, 32, 74, 116, 130, 132
  , simple queue 2, 108
  , single server queue 1, 13, 19

Random walk 2, 7, 17, 19, 59
  , maximum and minimum 24, 51, 52
  , modified 55
  , reflected 31
  , two-dimensional 111
Recurrence relation 7, 45
Regenerative property 96
Renewal function 23, 48
Renewal process 22
Renewal-reward process 129, 131
Risk-reserve 5, 6
Rogozin, B.A. 128, 130, 132, 134
Rubinovitch, M. 128, 134
Ruin problem 5, 85

Safety loading 68
Seal, H.L. 9, 15
Smith, W.L. 17, 44, 64
Spitzer, F. 17, 27, 44, 64
Stable distribution xii, 74, 82
Stationary independent increments 69
Statistical equilibrium 28
Statistical inference 6

Steady state   7
Stirling's approximation   83
Stopping times   105
Storage model   4, 128
  , a second   92
  , continuous time   5, 65
  , generalized   73
  , limit theorems for a   89
  with random output   124, 131
Subordinator   129
Syski, R.   14

Takacs, L.   14
Tauberian theorem   97
Tijms, H.C.   9

Waiting time
  in priority systems   99
  in single server systems   1, 19, 27
Wald equation   53, 105
Wet period in a dam   79
Wiener−Hopf factorization   7, 17, 130
  for Lévy processes   82, 110, 117, 127, 128, 131
  for random walks   22, 46, 48, 55
Wiener−Hopf technique   17, 45, 116, 130
Workload   67, 100

Applications of Mathematics

Vol. 1
Deterministic and Stochastic Optimal Control
By **W.H. Fleming** and **R.W. Rishel**
1975. ix, 222p. 4 illus. cloth
ISBN 0-387-**90155**-8

Vol. 2
Methods of Numerical Mathematics
By **G.I. Marchuk**
1975. xii, 316p. 10 illus. cloth
ISBN 0-387-**90156**-6

Vol. 3
Applied Functional Analysis
By **A.V. Balakrishnan**
1976. x, 309p. cloth
ISBN 0-387-**90157**-4

Vol. 4
Stochastic Processes in Queueing Theory
By **A.A. Borvokov**
1976. xi, 280p. 14 illus. cloth
ISBN 0-387-**90161**-2

Vol. 5
Statistics of Random Processes I
General Theory
By **R.S. Lipster** and **A.N. Shiryayev**
1977. x, 394p. cloth
ISBN 0-387-**90226**-0

Vol. 6
Statistics of Random Processes II
Applications
By **R.S. Lipster** and **A.N. Shiryayev**
1978. x, 339p. cloth
ISBN 0-387-**90236**-8

Vol. 7
Game Theory
Lectures for Economists and Systems Scientists
By **N.N. Vorob'ev**
1977. xi, 178p. 60 illus. cloth
ISBN 0-387-**90238**-4

Vol. 8
Optimal Stopping Rules
By **A.N. Shiryayev**
1978. x, 217p. 7 illus. cloth
ISBN 0-387-**90256**-2

Vol. 9
Gaussian Random Processes
By **I.A. Ibragimov** and **Y.A. Rosanov**
1978. x, 275p. cloth
ISBN 0-387-**90302**-X

Vol. 10
Linear Multivariable Control: A Geometric Approach
By **W.M. Wonham**
1979. xi, 326p. 27 illus. cloth
ISBN 0-387-**90354**-2

Vol. 11
Brownian Motion
By **T. Hida**
1980. xvi, 325p. 13 illus. cloth
ISBN 0-387-**90439**-5

Vol. 12
Conjugate Direction Methods in Optimization
By **M. Hestenes**
1980. x, 325p. 22 illus. cloth
ISBN 0-387-**90455**-7

Vol. 13
Stochastic Filtering Theory
By **G. Kallianpur**
1980. approx. 304p. cloth
ISBN 0-387-**90445**-X

Vol. 14
Controlled Diffusion Processes
By **N.V. Krylov**
1980. approx. 320p. cloth
ISBN 0-387-**90461**-1